THE SOUTHERN RICE INDUSTRY

Edited by
MARSHALL R. GODWIN
and
LONNIE L. JONES

Texas A&M University Press
College Station, Texas

Published by Texas Agricultural Experiment Station
in cooperation with Arkansas Agricultural Experiment
Station; Louisiana Agricultural Experiment Station;
and Economic Research Service and Farmer Cooperative Service, United States Department of Agriculture.

Texas A&M University Press, 1970

Preface

This book had its origin in the need for a base study of the Southern rice industry and the response of research and service agencies to this need. It is the end product of a comparatively unique effort for agricultural economists. The uniqueness stems from the facts that the study was a joint effort by three land-grant universities and two agencies of the federal government and that it was conducted wtihout a formal organizational arrangement. The motivation and single unifying force involved was the determination of individual participants to study the Southern rice industry with all the completeness that they could command, and to do so within a relatively brief time span so the analysis would be of maximum value and use.

Perhaps the effort that resulted in this volume foreshadows the configuration of much research that is to come on the problems of agriculture. Considered in its totality, the magnitude of the task would have transcended the capabilities of any of the individual agencies or institutions had they elected to go it alone. The work thus constitutes an example of what can be accomplished through the massing of expertise and a unified approach to broad based economic problems in agriculture. The need for such an approach to many, and particularly the more fundamental, economic problems of agriculture is becoming increasingly visible. Much that needs to be done does not fit the mold of the project system traditionally used in the land-grant universities and the federal establishment. The work of the task force contained in this volume has frequently been used as an example, both in the profession and by commodity trade groups, of the fact that large scale problems can be dealt with in an effective manner. Perhaps the result will stir other groups to take a similar approach. Hopefully, the outcome will be a more effective discharge of the responsibilities that rest on agricultural economists who work in the public sector.

The several chapters of this book are independently authored, and it is important that the reader understand this fact. Given the scope of the work, it must be clear that not all of those who participated in its writing would reach complete accord. Further, it needs to be made especially clear that the view of the United States Department of Agriculture is reflected only in those chapters where individuals from this agency share in authorship.

Even though authorship responsibility must be clearly established, those who prepared the individual chapters did not proceed independently. From the inception of the problem through the development of final manuscript drafts, the effort was characterized by a high degree of interchange between task force participants. The chapter authors have benefited greatly from critiques of their colleagues.

Not all the participants in this study appear as authors on the chapters which follow. Several others contributed to the success of the study by providing advice and assistance at particularly critical stages in its development and execution. In light of the fact that such involvement is not acknowledged elsewhere, it seems appropriate at this point to indicate all those persons who participated substantially in the team effort. Here are the names and affiliations of those who were involved:

Richard S. Berberich, Farmer Cooperative Service,
　　U. S. Department of Agriculture

George B. Blair, American Rice Growers Association

Robert J. Byrne, Farmer Cooperative Service

Marshall R. Godwin, Texas A&M University

Warren R. Grant, Farm Production Economics Division,
　　U. S. Department of Agriculture

Reid M. Grigsby, Louisiana State University

Lonnie L. Jones, Texas A&M University

Gene F. Miller, Farmer Cooperative Service,
U. S. Department of Agriculture

William R. Morrison, University of Arkansas

Troy Mullins, Farm Production Economics Division,
U. S. Department of Agriculture

E. P. Roy, Louisiana State University

Job K. Savage, Farmer Cooperative Service,
U. S. Department of Agriculture

Carl E. Shafer, Texas A&M University

Randall Stelly, Texas A&M University

Harlon D. Traylor, Louisiana State University

Fred H. Tyner, Louisiana State University

W. C. Verlander, Jr., New Orleans Bank for Cooperatives

We wish to express profound gratitude for the substantial assistance obtained from representatives in the rice industry, agencies of state and federal government, international organizations and others. Without the unstinting assistance from many such persons, the effort culminating in this book would have been considerably more difficult, and perhaps not possible at all.

Much credit is also due the staff of the Department of Agricultural Information at Texas A&M University. The rather considerable burden of editing and the logistics of production fell on these people. The high caliber of their performance will become clear as one examines the graphic and tabular presentations and general format of this book.

We feel that signal recognition is due the officers, staff and membership of the American Rice Growers Association in Lake Charles, Louisiana. Not only did this organization provide much assistance in the conduct of this study, but it also made a financial grant which may well have been the catalyst that made publication of this volume possible.

March 1, 1969

Marshall R. Godwin
Lonnie L. Jones

Contents

A Point of Departure:
The Need, the Organization
And the Setting

Lonnie L. Jones
Marshall R. Godwin

Change is the keystone of the dynamic society in which we work and live. Success in our fluid social and economic environment requires continual assessment of trends that indicate adjustments that should be made in order that business operations will be closely attuned to future conditions. This ongoing evaluation process is as much a requirement of business management as are those decisions necessary to sustain day-to-day operations. It is as necessary to agriculture as to other sectors of our economy.

The informational inputs that agricultural decision-makers use in adjusting to the future are winnowed from many sources. They are derived from the data generated and the observations made by management during business operations. They often are provided by trade associations and commercial press activities. They may be obtained through the use of private consultants and special study teams, or these informational inputs may come from the work of public agencies.

Despite this wide diversity of sources and the substantial flow of information produced by them, more information is sometimes necessary to meet the needs of decision-makers in agriculture as they adjust to conditions of the future. This continuing flow intermittently requires augmentation of a general view of events and forces which are afoot and an interpretation of what these events and forces mean in terms of industry-wide adjustments for the future.

For the southern rice industry, such a need for augmentation developed during the summer of 1967. Economic researchers in the public sector recognized the need during a series of meetings in which industry representatives explained their problems and identified the general areas of indecision and uncertainty with which they were confronted. Representatives from both state and federal agencies having research or service responsibility to the rice industry participated in these meetings. From their interchanges with those having a business orientation, there emerged a generally articulated requirement for the rice industry: a base study of the economic trends and social forces which would be relevant to the rice industry in the future. This study would re-establish a frame of reference within which industry decision-makers could engage in the ongoing process of evaluation and within which an appropriate strategy of industry adjustment could be developed to better accommodate the requirements of the future.

The responsibility for such a study fell largely, and appropriately, on the state and federal research and service agencies. To meet this responsibility, a task force of researchers from such agencies was organized to examine the rice industry and to identify the major trends, and implications of these trends, for the future. This book is the end product of that task force. In this book an effort is made to pull together in a meaningful form the conventional knowledge regarding the economics of the rice industry. But beyond this effort, the task force and the individual authors regarded their responsibility as one which transcended the assembling of past research information and published statistical data pertinent to the decision-making process in the rice industry. They viewed their charge as a broader obligation to supplement such information with the judgments and observations that could be made within the limits of their expertise and analytical capabilities regardless of the availability of the comfortable cloak of empirical evidence. This book, then, can be regarded as the maximum effort of the task force to meet the manifest needs of the rice industry for a new point of departure in its process of adjustment to remain compatible and competitive with the national economy in the years ahead.

ORGANIZATION OF THE BOOK

To carry out the examination with which the task force was charged, it was first essential to obtain a clear picture of the probable magnitude of future world rice needs and production. This required a detailed analysis of past production and consumption trends in the major rice regions of the world and the development of production and consumption projections for these regions. Trends in rice production and consumption in all major rice importing and exporting countries from 1948 to 1966 are examined in Chapter 2. In addition, a thorough examination is made of changes and trends in rice prices and stocks in rice producing countries and to per capita income and population growth in countries that are major consumers of rice.

An analysis of these trends, with allowances being made for anticipated changes in them, serves as the basis for the projections of rice production and consumption by major regions for the years 1975 and 1980. These projections are presented in Chapter 3.

From the evidence presented in these two chapters, the authors conclude that a substantial expansion in the world's need for rice will occur during the next 15–20 years, particularly in developing countries. Within this period, it is expected that a significant world rice deficit will develop when acreage and yield expansion fails to keep pace with increased demand for rice caused by population increases and higher consumer incomes.

The capability to expand U. S. rice output under existing farm legislation for rice and under alternative program arrangements is examined in Chapter 4. This capability is examined in light of the projected increases in world requirements and the possibility that U. S. rice production resources may play a prominent role in meeting these requirements. The conclusion is that substantial latent capacity exists for expanding U. S. rice production and that production goals in excess of existing levels could be attained if necessary. However, sustained increases in production substantially above present levels would require appropriate action to broaden the production base and to provide the necessary incentive for farmers to increase production. Such action would be somewhat contrary to past and present rice programs that have concentrated primarily on production restriction.

Chapter 4 also presents a detailed examination of alternative farm programs for rice that constitute plausible approaches to meeting the needs of the U. S. rice industry and other groups that are affected by policy implementation. The effects of a rice program are of primary importance to four major interest groups in the United States: rice producers, rice consumers, the rice marketing firm complex, and the federal government, the vehicle of program administration.

Each alternative program advanced is considered from one standpoint of the needs of various groups previously identified. An effort is made to emphasize the fact that a rice program may have widely varying consequences depending upon the vantage point from which it is considered. Further, conflicts of interest most probably will arise among groups, particularly the first three. This examination of alternatives from various relevant vantage points is designed to provide a reasonable framework for evaluating specific programs for use by those persons who must decide how policy should be addressed to the rice industry in the future.

The structure, efficiency, marketing and procurement practices and recent changes in the rice milling industry of the South are examined in Chapter 5. An analysis of recent changes and trends occurring within this highly competitive sector of the industry provides a basis for predicting probable number, size and organization of firms that will make up the future rice milling industry. Some of the major problems encountered by southern rice mills in procuring and marketing rice also are examined, and recommendations are made for possible improvements.

The rough rice drying and storage sector of the southern rice industry is extremely important to rice producers, and a significant share of the marketing bill is spent for this service. In Chapter 6, the structure, efficiency and major economic problems of this sector of the industry are explored. Among the chief problems examined in this chapter are the excessive costs of drying and storing rice resulting from the highly variable requirements for facilities from year to year and the need for more facilities per unit because of the shorter harvest season that has emerged in recent years. A detailed analysis of drying and storage costs is presented, and methods by which these costs may be reduced are advanced. Special attention is given to the feasibility of commingling rough rice at the primary level of exchange.

A comparison of transportation rates and services among major rice producing areas is made in Chapter 7. Detailed information is presented and analyzed on inland or domestic rail and truck transport rates for rice being moved from representative drying points through milling points to principal markets. A thorough analysis also is made of water transport rates for rice. Although the quantity of rice transported by water to domestic markets is insignificant, this mode of transportation is extremely important to the export operations of all rice producing areas. Hence, a comparison is made of the movement of rice into export channels by major U. S. ports and of negotiated export rates on rice from these ports to selected foreign markets. These comparisons of methods of moving rice and comparisons of transport practices within methods serve as a basis for recommending changes in the rice transportation system of the Gulf area.

The actions of the federal government, especially those involving export subsidies and the distribution of rice through domestic and foreign aid programs, exert a direct and significant influence on the operational and pricing efficiency of the U. S. rice industry. The role of these government activities is examined in Chapter 8. The purpose and operation of each of these programs is discussed thoroughly, and an analysis is made of the impact that past operations of these programs have had on producers and other sub-sectors of the rice industry. Recommendations then are made for improvements that could foster better understanding between the private and public sectors and which should lead to more effective operation of these programs in the future.

Chapter 9 examines alternative approaches to higher levels of market organization by growers in the southern rice area and the potentials that such organizations may have for the industry. The discussion centers chiefly on the potential for grower organization in the Gulf area of Louisiana and Texas. The prospect for efficiency gains in marketing rice in this area is analyzed by drawing upon the past experience in horizontal and vertical integration by producers in Arkansas and California. The chapter examines the current level of market organization, federal and state enabling legislation, and the capability to expand or extend the degree of organization within the present framework. The potential benefits of a higher level of organization or a changed organizational structure are pointed out, with particular attention being given to the prospects for increased marketing efficiency and improved bargaining power. From this analysis, the authors recommend changes in industry organization that may be made within the Gulf area to produce a more effective and efficient rice production and marketing system.

THE SOUTHERN RICE INDUSTRY IN PERSPECTIVE

The remainder of this introductory chapter is devoted to a general description of the southern rice industry in terms of its position in the U. S. and world rice economies and of its importance to the economies of the southern rice producing states. This description provides the reader with the setting within which the more detailed analysis of the following chapters takes place.

Rice is a somewhat unique product as compared with other major food crops of the world. This uniqueness stems from the fact that the world supply of rice is produced and consumed primarily in densely populated, developing countries. Rice is the basic daily diet for more than one-half of the world population and furnishes the basis for economic livelihood for millions of farmers and other persons engaged in rice marketing, distribution and related businesses in these developing areas of the world. In most producing countries, rice is grown as a subsistence crop. Hence, less than one-half of world rice production enters commercial market channels; a much smaller fraction enters world trade.

Within this general production-trade framework, the position of the United States is a conspicuous exception. In the United States, virtually all rice is marketed commercially, and a substantial share is exported. In 1967, for example, more than 60 percent of all rice grown in the United States found outlets abroad—through either commercial export channels or various governmental foreign aid programs. Although U. S. rice accounts for only about 2 percent of world production, this heavy export activity, together with the subsistence nature of the rice economies elsewhere, results in U. S. exports usually accounting for about one-fifth of total international trade in this commodity.

Compared to other rice producing countries, the United States stands in sharp contrast from the standpoint of domestic rice consumption. Per capita consumption of rice in most major rice producing countries ranges from 200 to 300 pounds per year, whereas U. S. consumers use rice at a much lower annual rate of about 7 pounds per capita. This low level of domestic consumption and the heavy export activity clearly indicate the dependence of the U. S. rice industry on world market outlets. Perhaps more importantly, these factors suggest the sensitivity of domestic market prices to changes that affect the economies of the major rice producing and consuming countries of the world.

Most of the U. S. rice supply is produced in Louisiana, Arkansas, Texas and California. These four states produce about 97 percent of the total domestic supply, with the three southern states producing slightly more than three-fourths of the U. S. total. Rice is produced also in several other states, but their aggregate contribution to total supply is minor, Table 1-1. Acreage devoted to rice and total production in the southern states historically has been rather evenly distributed among three general areas. These are the Arkansas and the Mississippi River Delta, Southwest Louisiana and the Coast Prairie of Texas.

Southern rice producers have experienced varying supply situations in recent years. Between 1945 and 1954, scarce supplies and strong world prices created a profitable position for most U. S. rice producers. Acreage of rice harvested in the South expanded rapidly during this period. This expansion and concomitant increases in acreage and production in other countries greatly increased world rice supplies. As a result, prices received for rice by U. S. producers in the mid-1950's fell to levels below the U. S. support price, and large

TABLE 1-1. PRODUCTION OF U.S. RICE IN MAJOR PRODUCING STATES, 1967

	Production, 1,000 cwt.	Percent of U.S. total
Missouri	235	0.3
Mississippi	2,365	2.6
Arkansas	21,465	23.9
Louisiana	22,035	24.6
Texas	25,908	28.9
California	17,640	19.7
Total U.S.	89,648	100.0

quantities of rice accumulated in Commodity Credit Corporation stocks. As a result of this excess supply situation, acreage allotments and marketing quotas were instituted for rice in 1955.

Since 1955, production has continued to increase in the southern region. However, increases during this period have resulted not from acreage expansion but almost solely from rapid increases in yields. Rice farmers have been receptive to technological advances growing out of public and private research. In all but 2 of the 13 crop years since rice acreage allotments and marketing quotas were adopted in 1955, rice yields per acre have been increasingly higher. The recent introduction of short season rice varieties has permitted Texas farmers to double crop their acreage and thereby increase production more rapidly than producers elsewhere in the country. As a result, Texas' share of the national rice supply has increased in recent years. In 1967, this share was about 29 percent, and it appears that Texas may become a perennial leader in future domestic rice production.

Cash farm receipts from the sale of rice nationally amounts to only about 2 percent of total cash receipts from crops. However, in the major southern rice producing states, it is of much greater importance. In 1967, cash receipts to producers from the sale of rice accounted for 28.4 percent of total cash receipts from crops in Louisiana, 23.4 percent in Arkansas and 11.5 percent in Texas, Table 1-2. In 1967, rice was the most important farm income crop in Louisiana, and it ranked third in both Texas and Arkansas. For the three-state region as a whole, cash receipts from rice sales were 17.4 percent of total receipts from all crops, making rice the second most important crop.

TABLE 1-2. IMPORTANCE OF CASH RECEIPTS FROM RICE TO PRODUCERS IN MAJOR SOUTHERN RICE PRODUCING STATES, 1967

| State | Cash receipts | | Rice as a percent of all crops | Rank among all crops |
	All crops	Rice		
	— — 1,000 dollars — —		Percent	Rank
Texas	1,153,007	133,064	11.5	3
Louisiana	378,030	107,509	28.4	1
Arkansas	426,683	99,679	23.4	2
Southern states	1,957,720	340,252	17.4	2

Source: Adapted from "Cash Receipts from the Sale of Texas Farm Commodities, 1966-67," Bulletin 48, Texas Crop and Livestock Reporting Service; "Distribution of Louisiana Cash Farm Income—1967" (mimeographed release), Louisiana Crop and Livestock Reporting Service; and "1967 Agricultural Statistics for Arkansas," Report Series No. 172, Crop Reporting Service, SRS, USDA, Little Rock, Arkansas.

These statistics indicate the economic importance of rice to producers in the southern rice industry and to the agriculture of this rice producing region. Accompanying this production is a complex system of firms engaged in storing, processing and marketing rice and in providing other services to rice producers. This production and marketing system is a significant element in the general economy of the southern rice producing region.

2

World Production, Exports, Prices and Consumption

Carl E. Shafer
Warren R. Grant

TRENDS IN PRODUCTION

Rice, the world's principal food crop and the daily staple for more than half of its total population, provides the economic livelihood for millions of families. Rice is grown on all continents, but Asiatic countries dominate world production.

World Trends

World rice production increased by 69 percent between 1948 (3,500 million hundredweight) and 1967 (5,900 million hundredweight), Figure 2-1. This upward trend in production can be attributed to increases in both acreage and yield. During the years in which world production declined, acreage harvested decreased, and yields either decreased or remained relatively unchanged. Average world yields improved by 31 percent between 1948 (1,410 pounds per acre) and 1964 (1,847 pounds per acre) while harvested acreage increased 24 percent during this same period.[1]

Regional Trends

Asia (including Communist countries) provides more than 90 percent of the world's rice supply, and changes in factors determining the production in this region necessarily influence world production significantly. Production, yield and acreage in Asia (excluding mainland China) follow a generally upward trend with a production increase of 55 percent between 1948 and 1967, Figure 2-1.[2] It is important to note that all other major world production regions

---

[1]Data on total world yields and harvested acreage were not available 1965-67 when submitted for publication.

[2]Mainland China is the major rice producing country in the world. However, production yield and acreage data are not readily available from this country. For this reason the data for Asia excludes this country. The Food and Agricultural Organization of the United Nations does include an allowance in the world totals for countries with missing data, thus mainland China's statistics are only in the world estimates shown above. Recent estimates suggest that mainland China produces about one-third of the world's rice.

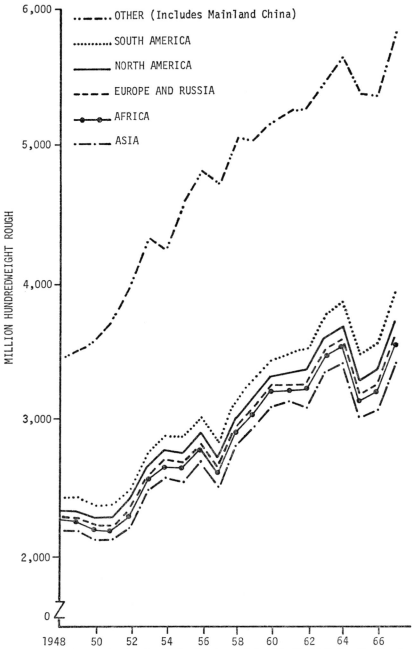

Figure 2-1. Rice Production by Major Regions of the World, 1948-67. (Production indicated by vertical distance between adjacent lines.)

10

had proportionately higher increases in production than Asia. Asian rice yields are lower than world yields. This difference has become more pronounced during recent years: world yields increased 31 percent during 1948-64 while Asian yields increased only 25 percent. Since more than one-half of the rice in Asia is nonirrigated, Asia's relatively low yields are due in part to dependency upon uncertain rains.

Harvested acreage in Asia, which is well over 90 percent of the world total when mainland China is included, increased 24 percent between 1948 and 1964.

In Africa, which produced only 2.4 percent of the world's rice in 1967, production increased 76 percent between 1948 and 1967, Figure 2-1.[3] This increase can be attributed to yield and acreage increases of 32 percent each between 1948 and 1967.

Production rose sharply in Europe in the early 1950's (from 23.1 million hundredweight in 1948 to 39.7 million hundredweight in 1953), declined slightly in the mid 1950's and has increased slightly since the mid 1950's, Figure 2-1. However, Europe's production was only 0.7 percent of the world total in 1967. Yields in Europe, which are more than double the average world yields, increased 31 percent between 1948 and 1967. Acreage harvested increased rapidly in the early 1950's but has remained relatively stable since this period.

Rice production more than doubled in North America (including Central America) between 1948 and 1967, increasing from 49.3 million hundredweight in 1948 to 116.1 million hundredweight in 1967, Figure 2-1.[4] Nevertheless, the 1967 production of this region amounted to only 2 percent of the world total. The increase in production is due primarily to yields which improved 71 percent between 1948 and 1967. Harvested acreage increased rapidly in the early 1950's; however, in 1955, acreage controls were applied in the United States, the major producer in this region. These controls resulted in a rather stable acreage during the remainder of the period.

Rice production in South America, 3.8 percent of the world total in 1967, has risen sharply from 79.0 million hundredweight in 1948 to 222.4 million hundredweight in 1967, an increase of 182 percent, Figure 2-1. This growth in production is primarily due to an almost threefold increase in acreage harvested. In 1948, 5.1 million acres of rice were harvested; by 1967, this acreage had increased to more than 14.5 million. Yields in South America are lower than average world yields and have remained relatively stable during this period.

The greatest rate of production increase has been attained in two minor producing regions, Russia and Oceania, with both areas

---

[3]United Arab Republic data is included with African data.
[4]Includes the Caribbean nations.

more than tripling their production between 1948 and 1967. However, these areas make up less than 0.4 percent of the total world production.

Major Exporting Country Trends

Burma's rice production increased from 117.4 million hundredweight in 1948 to 165.3 million hundredweight in 1967, a 41 percent increase, Figure 2-2. This increase can be attributed to both acreage (21 percent) and yield (14 percent) increases. Burma's production

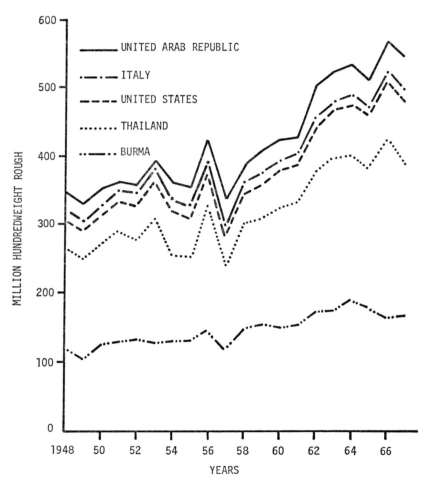

Figure 2-2. Rice Production by Major Exporting Countries, 1948-67. (Production indicated by vertical distance between adjacent lines.)

12

peaked at 187.6 million hundredweight in 1964. Thailand's production increased from 150.7 million hundredweight in 1948 to 261.1 million hundredweight, three times that of the United States, in 1966. A drouth in 1967 cut Thailand's production about 15 percent from the previous year. U. S. production more than doubled, from 38.3 million hundredweight to 89.4 million hundredweight, between 1948 and 1967 because of increased yields per acre. Although the United States has the potential land and water resources for more than doubling its acreage, government programs have held rice acreage relatively stable since 1955. Yields have more than doubled since 1948. In Italy rice production has remained relatively stable since 1956. Neither yields nor acreage has changed significantly. In the United Arab Republic rice production has almost doubled since 1948 due largely to increased acreage. Yields peaked at 5,210 pounds per acre in 1962. Since then, they have declined to the 1948-54 level.

Thailand was the leading producer among the major exporters in 1967-68, followed by Burma and the United States, Table 2-1.

Major Importing Country Trends

Indonesia's production increased 54 percent from 1948 to 1967, Figure 2-3, largely due to an increase in acreage of about 4.4 million acres between 1950 and 1964. Only slight improvements in yields occurred over the same period. India, the world's second largest producer after mainland China, increased production 74 percent from 1948 to 1967. India produced 1,200 million hundredweight in 1964, but, because of drouths, dropped to 1,000 million hundredweight in 1965 and 1966. The 1967 production, estimated at 1,300 million hundredweight, resulted from improved weather and increased inputs. India's yields are among the lowest in the world. Ceylon, although a small

TABLE 2-1. RICE PRODUCTION IN MAJOR RICE EXPORTING COUNTRIES AS PROPORTION OF WORLD TOTAL, 1967-68

Country	Rice production	
	Quantity	Proportion of world
	Million cwt.	Percent
Burma	169.8	2.9
Thailand	246.4	4.2
United States	89.5	1.5
Italy	16.6	0.3
United Arab Republic	50.6	0.9
Total	572.9	9.7

Sources: USDA, *The World Agricultural Situation*, Foreign Agricultural Economics Report No. 50, ERS, Washington, D. C., February 18, 1969.

―――――――――――, *Rice Situation*, RS-13, ERS, Washington, D. C., March 1969.

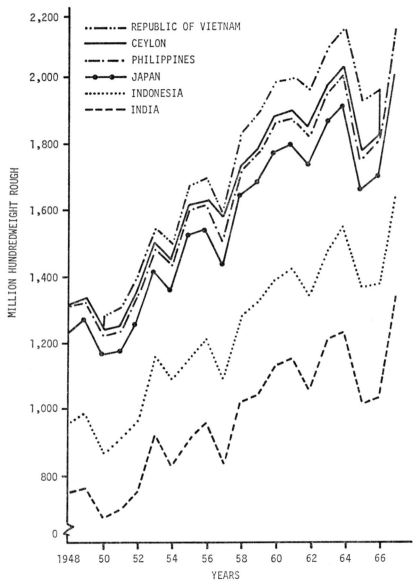

Figures 2-3. Rice Production by Major Importing Countries, 1948-67. (Production indicated by vertical distance between adjacent lines.)

14

producer, has almost tripled its rice production since 1948. This rapid increase can be attributed about equally to acreage and yield increases. Japan's production, acreage and yield have remained relatively stable since 1955, while rice production in the Philippines has risen 77 percent from 54.9 million hundredweight in 1948 to 97 million hundredweight in 1967. The Philippine increase resulted largely from acreage increases, since yields increased only 18 percent between 1948 (1,026 pounds) and 1966 (1,208 pounds). However, some improvements in yield occurred in 1967 and may continue as improved varieties are adapted. The Republic of Vietnam, once a major rice exporter, is currently a major importer. Production rose from 48.7 million hundredweight in 1950 to 117.4 million hundredweight in 1963 but dropped to 101.4 million hundredweight in 1966 due to the war. In contrast with the other importing countries, yields in this country have shown considerable improvement.

U. S. Trends

Since the end of World War II, U. S. rice farmers have experienced two supply situations for rice, Figure 2-4. The first, a continued period of scarce supplies and favorable prices in the world, resulted in rapid growth in acreage and production during the early 1950's. The second, a period of restricted acreage, started in 1955 and continues to the present. The 1967 acreage of 2.0 million acres was only 77 percent of the 1954 peak acreage. However, the 90 million hundredweight produced in 1967 is considerably above the 64.2 million hundredweight produced in 1954. When acreage restrictions were imposed, rice production was so intensified that yields increased more than 500 pounds per acre during the first year of allotments. Since then, with acreage allotments remaining in effect, yields have continued to rise about 124 pounds per year. The estimate for 1967, 4,550 pounds per acre, is more than double the 1948 yield of 2,122 pounds per acre. Much of this increase can be attributed to intensified production brought about by acreage restrictions; to technological changes such as new and better varieties, more effective herbicides, and higher and more timely fertilizer applications; and to the competitive drive of rice farmers who adopted these innovations rapidly.

Rice production for 1968, on the 2.4 million acres allotment base, is estimated at 105 million hundredweight, 18 percent greater than 1967 and 42 percent above the 1962-66 average.

Four states, Arkansas, California, Louisiana and Texas, produced about 97 percent of the 1968 U. S. production. Since 1948, each of these states at one time or another has led in production. With the introduction of stubble crop rice in 1962, Texas has enlarged its share of U. S. production. Since acreage controls hold the relative pro-

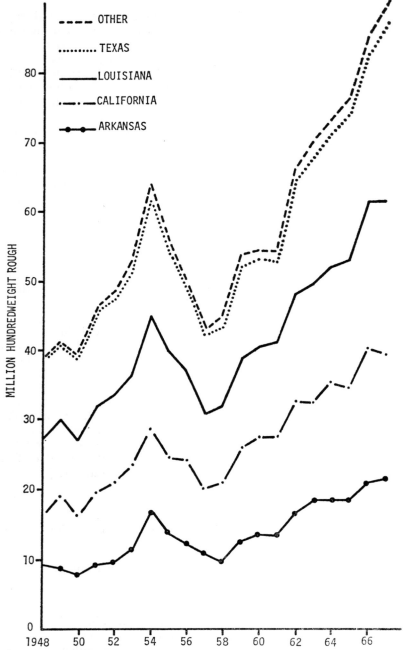

Figure 2-4. Rice Production by States in the United States, 1948-67. (Production indicated by vertical distance between adjacent lines.)

portions of acreage between states constant, the year-to-year variations in share of U. S. production have resulted from yield fluctuations within each state.

World Rice Stocks

Total world rice supply in any year consists of production plus carryover stocks. It appears that world rice carryover is a minor part of each year's supply. Among the major rice consuming countries, only Japan had significant carryover stocks. World carryover for exports in the Far East plus U. S. carryover varied from 1.4 percent to less than 0.5 percent of world production during 1954-66, Table 2-2. In recent years, U. S. carryover represented from one-third to one-half of the world's total carryover for export. Among the major exporting and importing countries of the world, excluding mainland China, Japan maintained the largest carryover, not for export, of 50.1 million hundredweight (rough) in 1966. That same year, India, the United States, Taiwan, the Philippines, East Pakistan and Ceylon all carried over more than 3.3 million hundredweight (rough).[5]

United States rice stocks varied considerably during 1948-67, Table 2-3. U. S. rough rice carryover averaged 2.8 percent of production during 1948-50, increased to 28.2 percent during 1955-57 and fell to 6.6 percent during 1965-67. Increased acreage and production in the early 1950's, especially 1954 (2.6 million acres seeded), resulted in increased carryover and reduced prices in the mid-1950's, Table 2-3.

Thus, while carryover stocks appear to be of little significance in the world supply situation, stocks are relevant in the U. S. domestic

[5]United Nations, FAO, *Rice Report 1967*, Rome 1967.

TABLE 2-2. WORLD RICE CARRYOVER: FAR EAST EXPORTERS AND THE U.S. AND WORLD RICE PRODUCTION, 1954, 1959 AND 1962-66

	Year						
	1954	1959	1962	1963	1964	1965	1966
	— — — — — — Million cwt. rough[1] — — — — — —
Carryover stocks[2]							
Far East exporters[3]	56.78	15.03	13.36	16.70	16.70	16.70	6.68
United States	8.02	16.36	5.58	8.12	7.95	8.12	8.65
Total	64.80	31.39	18.94	24.82	24.65	24.82	15.33
World production	4,400.38[4]	5,070.58[5]	5,308.68	5,509.29	5,564.40	5,773.84	5,546.77
Stocks as percent	1.47	0.61	0.35	0.45	0.44	0.43	0.28

[1]Converted from milled at 66 percent rate.
[2]Far East: stocks available for export only as of December 31; United States, August 1.
[3]Excluding mainland China.
[4]1953-55 average.
[5]1957-61 average.
Source: United Nations, FAO, *Commodity Review 1966*, Rome, p. 56 and 1967, p. 44.

TABLE 2-3. ROUGH RICE: SUPPLY AND DISTRIBUTION OF U.S. CROP AND AVERAGE FARM PRICE, 1948-67

Crop year	Supply			Distribution					Ending stocks	Balancing item	U.S. farm prices
	Carry-over stocks	Production	Total	Disappearance							
				Domestic			Export	Total			
				Seed	Feed	Milled[1]					
											$/cwt.
						1,000 cwt.					
1948	186	38,275	38,461	2,066	327	33,897	680	36,970	1,211	+ 280	4.88
1949	1,211	40,769	41,980	1,832	304	37,122	696	39,954	1,965	+ 61	4.10
1950	1,965	38,820	40,785	2,295	210	35,829	469	38,803	2,300	— 318	5.09
1951	2,300	46,089	48,389	2,340	250	43,611	471	46,672	781	+ 936	4.82
1952	781	48,193	48,974	2,575	193	45,044	673	48,485	776	— 287	5.87
1953	776	52,834	53,610	3,103	194	46,660	846	50,803	3,427	— 620	5.19
1954	3,427	64,193	67,620	2,222	1,647	52,294	703	56,866	8,736	+2,018	4.57
1955	8,736	55,902	64,638	1,981	1,900	42,078	1,188	47,147	18,294	— 803	4.81
1956	18,294	49,459	67,753	1,735	944	50,406	789	53,847	14,268	— 389	4.86
1957	14,268	42,935	57,203	1,855	173	43,657	280	45,965	10,527	+ 711	5.11
1958	10,527	44,760	55,287	2,068	164	43,702	327	46,261	7,069	+1,957	4.68
1959	7,069	53,647	60,716	2,092	164	49,525	385	52,166	7,813	+ 737	4.59
1960	7,813	54,612	62,425	2,080	160	52,046	379	54,665	7,341	+ 420	4.55
1961	7,341	54,198	61,539	2,329	[2]	55,387	79	58,399	3,140	+ 604[2]	5.14
1962	3,140	66,045	69,185	2,366		60,786	143	63,531	5,654	+ 236	5.04
1963	5,654	70,269	75,923	2,424		68,264	105	70,736	5,187	+ 57	5.01
1964	5,187	73,166	78,353	2,463		70,974	126	73,448	4,905	— 139	4.90
1965	4,905	76,281	81,816	2,702		70,595	169	75,706	5,475	+2,920	4.93
1966[3]	5,480	85,060	90,540	2,702		80,210	161	84,350	6,190	+1,777	4.77
1967[3]	6,190	90,614	96,804								

[1] Incudes an allowance for huller milling.
[2] Feed carried in balancing item (or residual).
[3] Preliminary.
Source: USDA, Rice: Annual Market Summary, C&MS, annual issues.

program as reflected in Commodity Credit Corporation acquisitions during low world prices—high production years of the mid-1950's. In recent years both total U. S. carryover and CCC stocks have been relatively low: 4.9 and 0.6 million hundredweight, respectively, in 1965 compared with 14.3 and 12.0 million hundredweight, respectively, in 1957.[6]

IMPORTS AND EXPORTS

World Exports

Throughout the world, rice is consumed largely in the country in which it is produced. Exports, including re-exports, were around 2.7 percent of total world production during 1957-61 and 1963-65. Although total exports are relatively small, the Gross Domestic Products (GDP) of some developing countries are significantly linked to their rice production and trade. Table 2-4 indicates the general importance of exports and imports for the major rice producing and consuming countries with the exception of mainland China which produced about one-third of the world's rice during 1961-63.

A significant change in the world rice market in recent years has been the change in status of the Republic of Vietnam from an exporter, 4.4 percent of world exports in 1963-64, to an importer, with 1968 imports estimated at 840,000 tons.[7]

The developing countries ranked by the economic importance of rice as measured by percentage of GDP during 1963-64 were Cambodia, the Republic of Vietnam, Burma, Thailand, Indonesia, India, Ceylon, Philippines, Japan and the United Arab Republic. Rice was extremely important in the foreign trade earnings of Burma, Cambodia, Thailand and the Republic of Vietnam but was a relatively large part of the purchases of Ceylon. The United States had only 1.3 percent of the world production but almost 19 percent of the world exports during 1961-63. India had 19 percent of the world production while importing 7 percent of the world exports. The United States was second only to Thailand in world exports according to 1966 estimates and moved into first place during 1967.

Only four countries—United States, Thailand, Burma and mainland China—have a current export potential of more than a million tons (milled), and these presently account for three-fourths of the rice entering international trade.[8] Among these four countries, the

[6]U. S. Department of Agriculture, *Agricultural Statistics 1967*, Washington, Government Printing Office, 1967.

[7]U. S. Department of Agriculture, *The Far East and Oceania Agricultural Situation*, ERS-Foreign 223, April 1968.

[8]Ellis, L. B., "Trends in World Rice Production and Trade," Proceedings of Rice Technical Workers Meeting, Little Rock, July 1966.

19

TABLE 2-4. ECONOMIC IMPORTANCE OF RICE AMONG MAJOR EXPORTING AND IMPORTING COUNTRIES, 1963-64

Country	Area sown as percent total useable land	Estimated value as percent of GDP	Consumption per capita, pounds	Trade Volume Units, mills cwt.[1]	Trade Volume Percent of world exports	Percent of total trade value	Production as percent of world
Exporting							
Burma	59	14	302	46.56	19.2	62.0	3.1
Thailand	66	14	371	63.40	26.2	36.0	4.1
United States	4	0.1	7	45.16[2]	18.7	0.8	1.3
Cambodia	69	21	328	16.27	6.7	65.0	1.1
United Arab Republic	16	2	68	17.60	7.3	6.0	0.9
Republic of Vietnam	71	20		10.76	4.4	47.0	2.1
Importing							
India	21	11	156	17.10	7.1	2.0	19.2
Ceylon	23	8	231	22.00	9.1	17.0	0.4
Japan	54	6	258	13.86	5.7	0.7	6.7
Philippines	26	8	196	9.99	4.1	4.0	1.5
Indonesia	37	14	187	35.74	14.8		5.3
World total	8		60	242.07			

[1]Converted from milled to rough at 66 percent.
[2]Includes government assisted programs.
Source: United Nations, FAO, The State of Food and Agriculture, 1966, Rome, p. 138, Table IV-1.

United States is probably the only one which has significant potential for increasing exports. The U. S. share of total world exports increased from 13.3 percent during 1952-56 to 19.6 percent in 1965, dropping slightly to 19.4 percent in 1966. Mainland China, whose exports increased by 69 percent between 1965 and 1966, is apparently able to export rice only by importing substitute grains. China exports rice at relatively high prices, earning foreign exchange with which to import larger quantities of wheat. The developed areas—United States, Australia and Europe—supplied 22.8 percent of the world exports in 1966, Table 2-5. Japan, Ceylon and India were the major importers in 1966, Table 2-6. Indonesia's imports dropped significantly between 1964 and 1965-66.

World rice trade amounted to about 300.6 million hundredweight (rough equivalent) in 1938, dropped to less than 67 million hundredweight in 1945 and, as indicated in Figure 2-5, trended upward to about 250.5 million hundredweight in 1965. The United States generally has experienced an expanding market for its rice exports since 1950; Thailand has more or less held its own with Burma showing some decline in recent years due to internal policies.[9] Continued expansion in foreign trade, as implied in the linear extrapolation of the 1950-65 trend in Figure 2-5, will depend on the ability of surplus producing countries to export their production.

U. S. Exports

The U. S. rice industry depends heavily upon exports and government activities which affect export prices and quantities. About 58 percent of the U. S. 1966-67 total rice supply was moved through various export outlets; 58 percent of these exports were dollar sales (which involve export subsidies), and the remaining 42 percent were moved (largely to South Vietnam) under Public Law 480.[10]

Most U. S. rice exports are in milled form. During 1962-65, milled rice exports averaged 29.2 million hundredweight while rough rice exports averaged less than 200,000 hundredweight, Tables 2-3 and 2-7. During 1948-66, the proportion of total U. S. milled rice supplies exported varied from 36.9 percent during 1952-55 to 59.5 percent during 1963-66.

With the commencing of heavy CCC activities during the mid-1950's, the proportion of U. S. rice exports under specified government programs rose from 3.7 percent in 1954-55 to a high of 82.9 percent in 1956-57 when 69 percent was sold for foreign currency under Title I of Public Law 480, Table 2-8. Exports under govern-

[9]U. S. Department of Agriculture, *The Far East and Oceania Agricultural Situation,* ERS-Foreign 223, April 1968.

[10]U. S. Department of Agriculture, *Demand and Price Situation,* ERS DPS 114, November 1967.

TABLE 2-5. INDIGENOUS EXPORTS OF RICE BY REGIONS AND SELECTED COUNTRIES, 1934-38, 1952-56 AND 1957-59 AVERAGES AND ANNUALLY 1960-66[1]

Region and country	1934-38 average	1952-56 average	1957-59 average	1960	1961	1962	1963	1964 (Provisional)	1965 (Estimate)	1966 (Provisional)
					Million cwt. rough[2]					
Exporters										
Far East total	266.25	102.52	156.93	169.55	139.42	135.22	159.63	164.48	157.83	148.98
Burma	102.55	48.07	54.05	58.42	53.14	57.52	57.22	51.44	43.42	36.74
Cambodia	44.09[3]	5.48[3]	6.58	10.62	7.64	4.41	12.49	15.50	16.70	5.61
China mainland	0.57	16.40	37.98	39.48	12.49	18.81	21.08	23.88	21.71	36.74
Pakistan		3.51	.80	2.30	4.14	4.28	3.91	5.21	6.68	6.21
Thailand	46.36	41.79	42.29	40.12	52.24	42.56	47.37	61.23	61.80	50.34
Western Hemisphere	5.7	29.93	27.79	37.51	39.15	45.43	45.93	52.81	60.13	62.60
United States	2.4	22.65	23.11	33.30	27.94	35.07	39.98	44.39	48.43	45.16
Brazil	1.8	0.19	0.70		5.04	1.47		0.40	6.68	9.65
Africa and Near East	4.9	6.61	9.92	11.35	8.95	6.68	14.03	20.00	20.04	12.79
United Arab Republic	3.3	3.11	8.02	10.19	7.55	4.81	12.69	17.60	18.37	11.59
Europe	5.54	11.76	9.38	6.75	10.72	8.15	6.51	4.64	6.68	5.04
Italy	4.31	8.25	5.14	4.14	7.01	5.75	4.64	2.10	4.51	2.71
Oceania	0.33	1.10	1.50	2.37	1.90	1.74	1.90	2.10	2.34	2.84
Australia	0.33	1.10	1.50	2.37	1.90	1.74	1.90	2.10	2.34	2.84
World total	282.79	169.92	205.53	227.54	200.15	197.21	228.01	244.04	247.02	232.25

[1]Indigenous exports excludes re-exports.
[2]Converted to rough rice at 66 percent.
[3]Includes Vietnam.

TABLE 2-6. RETAINED IMPORTS OF RICE BY REGIONS AND SELECTED COUNTRIES, 1934-38, 1952-56 AND 1957-59 AVERAGES AND ANNUALLY 1960-66

Region and country	1934-38 average	1952-56 average	1957-59 average	1960	1961	1962	1963	1964	1965	1966 (Provisional)
						Million cwt. rough[1]				
Far East	206.20	116.71	122.05	128.90	124.53	113.00	137.39	151.28	146.93	141.23
Ceylon	17.70	13.92	17.60	17.64	15.63	13.73	13.46	21.98	25.05	17.04
India	72.15	14.53	16.80	23.82	13.56	13.42	16.94	21.54	21.71	26.25
Indonesia	8.72	15.13	23.54	32.13	35.57	35.54	35.74	36.74	8.35	8.78
Japan	57.85	36.68	12.59	5.85	4.21	5.95	7.42	14.03	28.39	26.52
Philippines	1.17	1.64	3.87		6.28		8.55	10.09	19.71	3.36
Africa and Near East	14.16	13.36	23.54	27.69	30.50	32.47	31.13	37.28	40.08	34.14
Europe	43.66	24.12	38.75	49.70	22.78	34.37	33.27	37.68	38.41	36.37
Western Hemisphere	14.83	10.56	13.23	13.76	13.03	10.96	12.36	17.20	15.53	15.93
Oceania	1.34	.87	1.30	1.34	1.54	1.47	1.50	1.47	1.50	1.50
World total	280.18	165.61	198.88	221.40	192.37	192.27	215.65	244.91	243.84	229.18

[1]Converted to rough rice at 66 percent.
Source: Ellis, Leonard B., "Trends in World Rice Production and Trade," *Proceedings, Rice Technical Working Group*, June 14-17, 1966, Little Rock, Arkansas; 1966 data from R. A. Bieber, FAS, USDA.

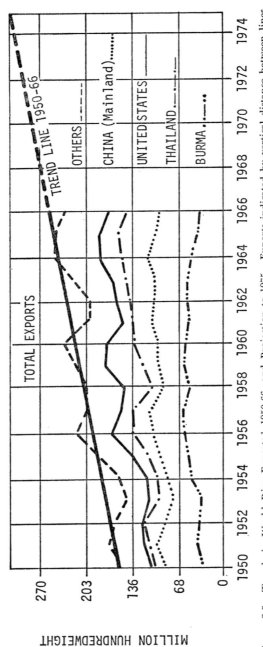

Figure 2-5. Trends in World Rice Exports,[1] 1950-66, and Projection to 1975. Exports indicated by vertical distance between lines.

[1]Rough Rice Equivalent, Converted from Milled Metric Tons Excuding Re-Exports.
Source: United Nations, FAO, *The State of Food and Agriculture* 1966, Rome, 6. 185.

24

TABLE 2-7. SUPPLY AND DISTRIBUTION OF U.S. MILLED RICE, 1948-66

Year beginning Aug. 1	Supply				Distribution					Ending stocks
	Carry-over stocks[1]	Production[2]	Imports	Total	Exports[3]	Shipment to territories	Consumed at breweries	Remaining for domestic food	Total	
					1,000 cwt.					
1948	381	23,510	37	23,928	9,509	3,379	2,989	7,284	23,161	767
1949	767	25,727	42	26,536	10,718	3,954	3,276	7,613	25,561	975
1950	975	24,775	544	26,294	9,036	3,485	3,367	8,868	24,756	1,538
1951	1,538	31,286	389	33,213	16,933	3,610	3,395	8,370	32,308	905
1952	905	31,318	243	32,466	16,722	3,602	3,165	8,455	31,944	522
1953	522	31,821	290	32,633	15,198	3,256	3,170	8,561	30,185	2,448
1954	2,448	36,180	45	38,673	9,391	3,876	3,882	8,962	26,111	12,562
1955	12,562	28,289	135	40,986	12,056	3,677	4,176	9,739	29,648	11,338
1956	11,338	35,174	268	46,780	25,637	3,634	3,549	9,993	42,813	3,967
1957	3,967	30,523	165	34,655	12,609	3,732	3,348	9,623	29,512	5,343
1958	5,343	30,438	115	35,896	13,528	3,940	3,278	9,160	29,906	5,990
1959	5,990	34,896	550	41,436	20,327	4,126	3,488	10,443	38,384	3,052
1960	3,052	36,928	203	40,183	20,640	2,830	3,482	11,288	38,240	1,943
1961	1,943	39,688	274	41,905	20,835	2,331	3,338	13,806	40,333	1,572
1962	1,572	43,275	25	44,872	25,190	3,127	2,888	12,166	43,394	1,478
1963	1,478	49,146	10	50,364	29,976	3,134	2,767	13,065	48,942	1,692
1964	1,692	51,041	338	53,071	30,489	3,566	3,095	13,926	51,076	1,995
1965	1,995	50,942	480	53,417	31,135	3,154	3,391	13,746	51,426	1,991
1966	1,991	58,381	3	60,375	37,740	3,732	3,819	13,400	58,691	1,684

[1]Includes government-owned stocks for 1954-57.
[2]Production of heads, second heads, screenings and brewer rice.
[3]Exports and imports from Bureau of the Census.
Source: USDA, Rice: Annual Market Summary, C&MS, 1957-67 issues.

TABLE 2-8. U.S. EXPORTS OF MILLED RICE UNDER SPECIFIED AND OUTSIDE SPECIFIED GOVERNMENT-FINANCED PROGRAMS, JULY-JUNE 1954-67

Fiscal year	Public law 480						P. L. 655	Total	Total[3]	Total exports	
	Title I	Title II	Title III		Title IV		Sec. 402, (sales for foreign currency and economic aid)	exports under specified government programs	exports outside specified government programs	Quantity	Percent under specified government programs
	Sales for foreign currency	Famine and other emergency relief	Foreign donation[1]	Barter[2]	Long-term credit						
						— 1,000 cwt. —					
1954-55		305		5			1	311	8,132	8,443	3.7
1955-56	2,530	1,943	865	197			563	6,089	5,477	11,575	52.6
1956-57	18,127	549	2,175	657			248	21,756	4,488	26,244	82.9
1957-58	5,094	483	596	8			153	6,334	5,463	11,797	53.7
1958-59	3,767	40	541	2,552				6,900	7,120	14,020	49.2
1959-60	9,960	575	1,417	683			162	12,797	7,435	20,232	63.2
1960-61	11,906	404	1,751	348			93	14,502	6,702	21,204	68.4
1961-62	8,612	440					494	9,546	10,787	20,333	46.9
1962-63	12,742	14			770		341	13,867	10,187	24,054	57.6
1963-64	13,211				1,072		593	14,876	16,814	31,690	46.9
1964-65	11,004				759		38	11,801	16,686	28,487	41.4
1965-66	6,917				716		2,008	9,641	20,683	30,324	31.8
1966-67	16,286				2,763			19,049	20,509	39,558	48.2

[1]Foreign donations are authorized under Sec. 416 of the Agricultural Act of 1949 and Sec. 302, Title III, P. L. 480.

[2]The barter program is authorized under the Charter Act of the Commodity Credit Corp.; Sec. 303, Title III, P. L. 480; and other legislation.

[3]"Agricultural exports outside government programs" (sales for dollars) include, in addition to unassisted commercial transactions, shipments of some commodities with governmental assistance in the form of (1) extension of credit, (2) sales of government-owned commodities at less than domestic market prices and (3) export payments in cash or in kind.

Source: USDA, *Rice, Annual Market Summary*, C&MS, 1961-67 issues.

ment programs rose significantly, from 32 to 48 percent, between 1965-66 and 1966-67. Export subsidies for rice were paid from 1958 through 1966, Table 2-9. The amount of the export subsidy was highest during 1960 and 1961, the two years when world prices were lowest during the 1948-65 period. With higher world rice prices, export subsidies were discontinued in mid-1967.

The southern rice production area of the United States has the largest share of U. S. production and exports, Table 2-10. California averaged about 21 percent of U. S. total rough rice production in 1965-67 while providing about 17 percent of U. S. total milled rice exports during the 1964-66 period. California's shipments of milled rice to U. S. territories during 1961-65 were about 3.5 times those of the Southern area, Table 2-10.

TABLE 2-9. WORLD AVERAGE EXPORT UNIT VALUE FOR MILLED RICE, U.S. EXPORT SUBSIDIES AND EXPORT PRICES FOR U.S. MILLED RICE, 1948-66

Year	World average export unit value of milled rice	Export subsidy[1]	Export price[2]	Export price plus subsidy
— — — — — — Dollars per cwt. — — — — — —				
1948	7.44	0	9.70	9.70
1949	6.90	0	7.70	7.70
1950	5.76	0	8.00	8.00
1951	6.13	0	8.70	8.70
1952	7.58	0	7.70	7.70
1953	8.32	0	9.90	9.90
1954	6.66	0	8.50	8.50
1955	5.34	0	7.70	7.70
1956	5.24	0	7.70	7.70
1957	5.24	0	7.60	7.60
1958	5.46	NA	7.90	7.90
1959	5.02	2.73	6.90	9.63
1960	5.03	2.91	6.60	9.51
1961	4.89	2.78	6.00	8.78
1962	5.47	2.25	6.70	8.95
1963	5.50	2.28	6.80	9.08
1964	5.67	2.22	7.16	9.38
1965	5.77	1.81	7.28	9.09
1966		0.87	7.79	NA

[1]Amount paid out for export payments divided by quantity exported (includes PL480 transactions). Source: Commodity Credit Corporation, *Report of Financial Condition and Operations.*

[2]A derived price (value) based on total value of U.S. rice exports divided by total quantity of U.S. rice exported. Source: *Statistical Abstract of the United States.* For 1964-66, *Foreign Agricultural Trade of the United States,* ERS, USDA.

Source: Data compiled by W. R. Grant, FPED, Texas A&M University, United Nations, FAO, *State of Food and Agriculture, 1966,* Rome, p. 238.

TABLE 2-10. U.S. MILLED RICE EXPORTS FROM SOUTHERN AREA AND CALIFORNIA, 1954-66

Year	Total supply		Exports		Exports as percent of total supply		Shipments to territories	
	Southern area	California	Southern area	California	Southern area	California	Southern area	California
	— — — — 1,000 cwt. — — — —						— 1,000 cwt. —	
1954	29,732	8,183	5,559	3,820	18.7	46.7	1,370	2,605
1955	34,223	5,916	12,046	84	35.2	.1	1,175	2,409
1956	36,237	9,922	20,174	4,379	55.7	44.1	1,013	2,821
1957	28,733	7,309	12,243	1,028	42.6	14.1	721	2,842
1958	24,758	9,850	10,275	3,302	41.5	33.5	513	3,123
1959	32,552	8,471	17,680	1,969	54.3	23.2	800	3,212
1960	31,908	9,408	18,246	2,634	57.2	28.0	675	2,762
1961	29,979	11,358	16,876	3,800	56.3	33.5	699	2,479
1962	33,931	10,868	20,404	4,806	60.1	44.2	678	2,321
1963	39,510	10,942	24,912	5,050	63.1	46.2	649	2,541
1964	41,556	11,418	25,848	4,650	62.2	40.7	730	2,501
1965	43,454	11,130	27,926	3,861	64.3	34.7	712	2,646
1966	45,968	15,720	30,296	8,798	65.9	56.0	915	2,843

Source: USDA, *Rice: Annual Market Summary*, C&MS, selected issues.

Long-grain rice from the southern area represented from 34 to 48 percent of U. S. total milled rice exports during 1962-65. Medium-grain rice from the Southern area was second in terms of the proportion of total exports with medium and short-grain rice from California ranking third. Most of the exported southern rice was milled, less than one-fifth was parboiled and the remainder was brown rice.

PRICES

World

Rice, varying by type, variety, method of processing and quality, enters world trade in several distinct classes. Export prices for major exporting countries tend to move together, but rice has no major international market such as that for wheat or cotton.[11] Furthermore, the heavy involvement of central governments in rice exporting results in price behavior other than that which might be expected under more "open market" conditions.[12]

[11]"An FAO Index of Export Prices of Rice," UN FAO *Monthly Bulletin of Agricultural Economics and Statistics*, 10 (11): 3-9, November 1961.

[12]Ideally, an econometric model of the world rice economy should be developed in order to explain and predict better the behavior of rice export prices and volumes. However, because of the absence of a major world market for rice and heavy government involvement in rice exporting, the probability of developing such a model successfully may be small. Nevertheless, such a model probably would prove enlightening. Questions regarding not only the behavior of prices and volumes but also foreign exchange would be relevant. Lacking a comprehensive model of the world rice export industry, a general discussion of major price levels and trends will have to suffice in this section.

In order to better judge the general movement of international rice prices, the U.N. Food and Agricultural Organization developed an index of export prices (1957-59 = 100) for rice which contains data beginning with 1957. Twenty-one international prices of various types, varieties and qualities of rice are included. Separate indexes for government-to-government contracts, private contracts and long/medium and round-grain rice are available.

The FAO overall index of rice export prices for 1957-65 seems to move rather closely with the Thailand and U. S. export price relatives, and the world export unit value relative in Figure 2-6. These four series are not mutually exclusive. U. S. and Thailand export prices tend to move together closely from 1948 to 1960 with the exception of 1951-52. If the export subsidies are added to the U. S. price during 1961-64, the U. S. price relative would be above that of Thailand during this period.

During the 17-year period, 1950-66, world annual unit export values moved opposite annual world export volumes in 10 of the 16 year-to-year periods, Figure 2-7. However, total export value and

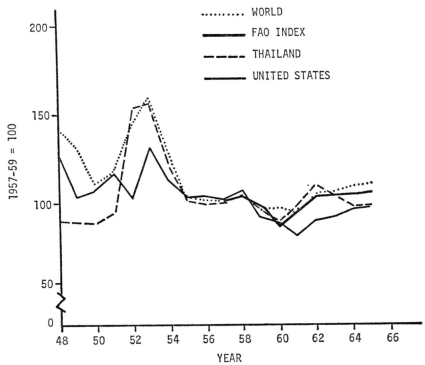

Figure 2-6. Price Relatives of Export Prices for U. S. and Thailand Milled Rice and World Export Unit Value, 1948-66. (1957-59 = 100)

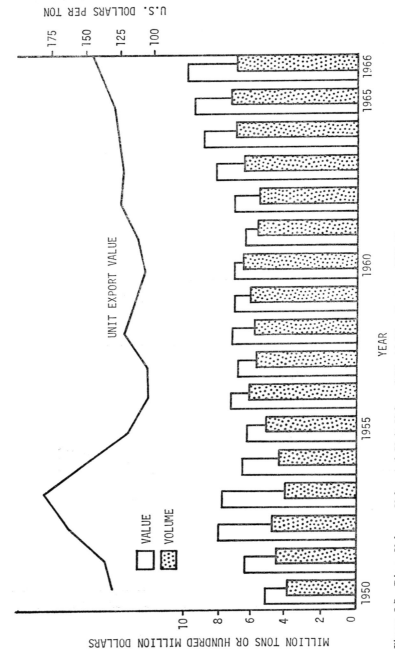

Figure 2-7. Rice: Volume, Value and Unit Value of World Rice Exports, 1950-66.
Source: United Nations, FAO, *Commodity Review*, 1966, Rome, p. 53.

total volume tended to be directly associated implying, in an overall sense, an elastic situation where "world prices" moved opposite to export volume but by a smaller percentage. Population growth and income affect prices and total values apart from volume. The tendency for world unit export values to move opposite to world export volume suggests that the main cause of price movements is on the supply side, as expected.

The rather indeterminate behavior of the world rice export market during 1950-65 makes it difficult, if not impossible, to forecast the volume of world rice trade and/or prices. Although total world exports are relatively stable, exports from individual countries may vary significantly.[13] Export variations are due to both world supply and demand and government stockholding and export price policies. Variations in exports can have serious effects on the economies of those countries in which rice accounts for a large share of the foreign exchange revenue.

FAO's export price indexes for private and bilateral contracts do not move together between 1962 and 1965; the private contract subindex dropped 6 points (105 to 99) while the government-to-government contract subindex rose 14 points (98 to 112). Similarly, divergence is found among types; the long/medium-grain subindex dropped 2 points (104 to 102) while the round-grain subindex increased 16 points (104 to 120); the total index increased 2 points during the period. Private trade constituted 48.5 percent of the 1957-59 export base weights with government contracts being the remaining 51.5 percent. Round-grain rice was only 14.4 percent of total base period exports.

All indices rose in 1966, reflecting the decline in world exports in the face of increasing demands of population and income pressures.

Major Countries

The variation in wholesale milled rice prices (reported separately from export prices *per se*) among selected exporting countries can be seen in Figure 2-8. The wholesale price relatives for the United States and Thailand paralleled each other from 1958 to 1965 while the United Arab Republic's price was practically unchanged for 1948 through 1963, presumably the result of a producer price fixing policy. Cambodia's price was quite variable and Brazil's price increased more than tenfold between the base period, 1957-59, and 1965. These prices were not deflated, and this is part of the problem in measuring real price changes among countries.[14] FAO estimates of actual and deflated

---

[13]United Nations, FAO, "Price Structure of the International Rice Market" (1957) and "Fluctuations in Exports and Prices of Rice" (1959) from *The World Rice Economy, Volume I, Selected Papers,* Commodity Bulletin Series 36, Rome 1962.

[14]Real or deflated prices are defined as actual prices divided by the respective cost-of-living or other price index.

wholesale milled rice prices for selected countries for four selected years are shown in Table 2-11. During the period, 1950-59, Thailand's deflated price index dropped to 69 in 1959 while neighboring Burma's rose to 117. The U. S. deflated price index dropped identically with Thailand's; Egypt's was stable while Japan's increased to 133. Brazil's and Indonesia's actual price indexes rose to 526 and 750 while their deflated price indexes were only 100 and 154, respectively. Thus, the indeterminacy of world rice prices is paralleled in domestic milled rice prices of major rice countries in which deflated prices moving in different directions and considerable divergence among actual prices are to be found.

The estimated unit value of exports, computed from total exports and total value, for Burma, Thailand, United States and United Arab Republic are shown in Figure 2-9. These data are reported by FAO in U. S. dollars. The U. S. export unit value was highest and moved closely on a year-to-year change basis with that of Thailand. Burma and Thailand export unit values moved inversely in four of the five periods between 1959 and 1964. The world export unit value increased

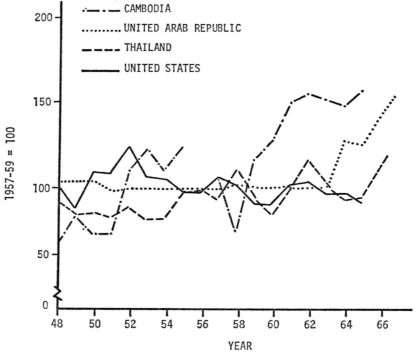

Figure 2-8. Price Relatives of Wholesale Milled Rice Prices of Selected Exporting Countries, 1948-66. (1957-59 = 100)

32

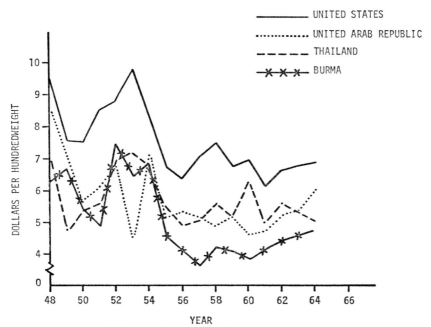

Figure 2-9. Unit Value of Exports for Selected Exporting Countries, 1948-64; Dollars Per Hundredweight of Milled Rice.

TABLE 2-11. INDEXES OF ANNUAL WHOLESALE PRICES OF MILLED RICE, ACTUAL AND DEFLATED BY COST OF LIVING INDEXES, 1950-59

Country	Price form	1950	1953	1956	1959
		— — — — — 1950 = 100 — — — — —			
India	Actual	100	112	102	112
	Deflated	100	107	98	93
Thailand	Actual	100	97	113	117
	Deflated	100	71	77	69
Egypt	Actual	100	95	95	103
	Deflated	100	94	95	100
U.S.A.	Actual	100	92	88	83
	Deflated	100	83	78	69
Italy	Actual	100	112	115	119
	Deflated	100	97	90	91
Burma	Actual	100	105	101	101
	Deflated	100	116	105	117
Japan	Actual	100	132	149	165
	Deflated	100	117	125	133
Indonesia	Actual	100	221	334	750
	Deflated	100	117	110	154
Brazil	Actual	100	217	288	526
	Deflated	100	135	103	100

Source: United Nations, FAO, *The World Rice Economy, Vol. II, Trends and Forces,* Commodity Bulletin Series 36, Rome 1963, p. 56.

33

about 12 percent between 1965 and 1966 due to a drop in exports. Although the world rice export price and volume situation is yet to be systematically analyzed, some work on an econometric model for U. S. rice has been accomplished.[15] Using this model, Grant estimated domestic and world export price elasticities for the United States (wholesale price level) at −0.27 and −1.54, respectively. The relatively high export elasticity makes the present U. S. "two-price" plan operational and is a requirement for any price discrimination scheme.

U. S. Domestic Prices

Farm Level

Rice prices differ depending upon (a) the stage—farm, wholesale or retail; (b) the variety—long, medium and short-grain; and/or (c) the form—head rice, second heads, screenings, brewer's rice, rice bran and rice polish and mill feed. Only U. S. prices received by farmers for all rice and for selected types by states and selected milled prices by types are presented here.

Prices received by farmers in the southern production area generally moved together during 1954-66 with Texas prices being slightly higher than other states in this region, Figure 2-10. Average prices received by California farmers (medium and short-grain rice) were below those of the southern area between 1954 and 1961, equivalent from 1962 to 1965 but sharply below in 1966. U. S. farm prices have been relatively stable since 1954 when CCC support activities were intensified. Present U. S. rice production is about double the 1956-57 level, but farm prices are about the same.

Varieties

The southern area produces mostly medium and long-grain rice while California produces short and medium-grain. The change in proportions among varieties has been considerable over time due to the frequent introduction of new varieties. Belle Patna, which was not available until 1961, constituted about 13 percent of U. S. production and 16 percent of southern production in 1967. Century Patna

---

[15]W. R. Grant reports the following equation for U. S. export prices for 1934-63 excluding 1941-45: $P_e = 18.343 - 0.020Q_e - 7.329Q_{w/p} + 0.190T_1$
t values (3.98)   (2.68)   (4.07)
$R^2 = 0.861$

where: P_e = average price received for U. S. rice exported less the export subsidy (in dollars per hundredweight of milled rice).

Q_e = total world exports of rice (in million hundredweight of rough rice).

$Q_{w/p}$ = per capita world production of rice (hundredweight per capita rough).

T_1 = time, 1934 = 1.

Source: Grant, W. R., "A Model for Estimating Costs of Government Export Programs for Rice," *Agriculture Economic Research*, 19 (3): 73-80, July 1967.

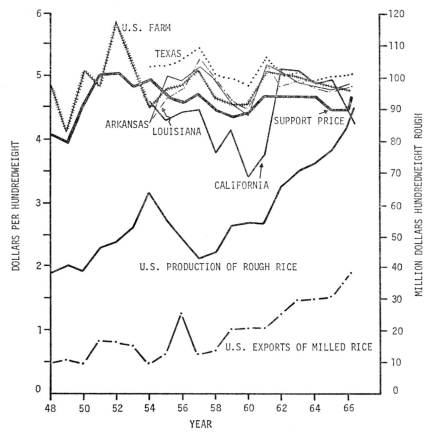

Figure 2-10. Prices Received by Farmers for Rough Rice in Arkansas, California, Louisiana and Texas, Annual Average, 1954-66; U. S. Average Farm Price, 1948-66, and Rough Rice Production and Milled Rice Exports, 1948-66.

represented about 11 percent of U. S. production in 1959 but only 0.12 percent in 1967. Bluebelle increased from 3.6 percent to 15.0 percent of the U. S. total production between 1966 and 1967. The dominant varieties during the 1959-67 period were Bluebonnet, Nato and California Pearl, Table 2-12.

Long-grain rice dropped from 50.4 to 48.5 percent of total U. S. production between 1959 and 1967 while medium-grain rice expanded from 29.2 to 42.3 percent of the total. Total long-grain production actually increased from 26.5 million hundredweight to 43.4 million hundredweight between 1959 and 1967, but medium-grain production more than doubled from 15.3 to 37.9 million hundredweight during

35

TABLE 2-12. VARIETIES OF RICE CONSTITUTING TOTAL PRODUCTION, U.S., 1959 AND 1967

Variety	Proportion of U.S. total production	
	1959	1967
	— — — — Percent — — — —	
Long grain		
Bluebonnet	33.4	17.4
Belle Patna		13.2
Century Patna	10.6	0.1
Total	50.4	48.5
Medium grain		
Nato	19.4	17.4
Roses (including Calrose)	3.5	10.7
Saturn		12.7
Total	29.2	42.3
Short grain		
Pearl (total)	20.4	9.2
Total	100.0	100.0

Source: Annual issues of *The Rice Journal*.

the same period. Pearl dropped from 10.7 to 8.2 million hundredweight while Calrose jumped from 1.3 to 9.6 million hundredweight over the 8-year period.[16]

On the basis of numbers of acres planted in 1967, the most important varieties in the southern states were Bluebonnet and Nato in Arkansas; Saturn, Nato and Bluebonnet in Louisiana; and Bluebelle, Belle Patna and Nato in Texas.

Price data by variety are difficult to compile because of the rather rapid turnover of varieties. However, the three predominant varieties in the southern states as of 1966 are in descending order of general prices f.o.b. mills and driers, Bluebonnet, Belle Patna (both long-grains) and Nato (medium-grain). These type of data have not been available for years after 1965.

Reasons for the differences, or lack of differences, among prices in the three states are not readily apparent.

Milled Rice Prices

Milled rice prices for Bluebonnet (long-grain) and for medium-grains at three southern markets moved together rather closely from 1948 through 1967, Figure 2-11. However, medium-grain prices dropped about a dollar per hundredweight between 1962 and 1965, from $9.25 to $8.20, while Bluebonnet prices remained stable or increased slightly at the $10.00 level. Prices for California medium-grain and short-grain rice increased rather steadily between 1958 and

[16]*The Rice Journal*, 1960 Annual Issue and January 1968 issue.

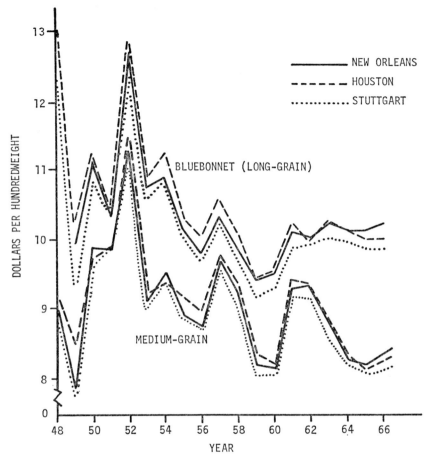

Figure 2-11. Milled Rice: Season Average Price for U. S. No. 2, Bluebonnet and U. S. No. 2 Medium-Grain at Southern Markets, 1948-66.

1965 while Southern medium-grain rice prices trended downward, Figure 2-12. This situation is reflected at the New York market where Bluebonnet and California Pearl prices generally increased during the 1960-66 period while medium-grain prices generally declined from 1962 to 1966, Figure 2-13.

The departure of medium-grain prices from long and short-grain prices during the 1960's while the overall U. S. farm price was stable, except for the 1960-61 increase, may be due to the change in the proportions of these types. While U. S. total rice production increased by 65.4 percent between 1961 and 1967, long-grain rice increased from 45.3 to 48.5 percent and short-grain rice dropped from 16.3 to

37

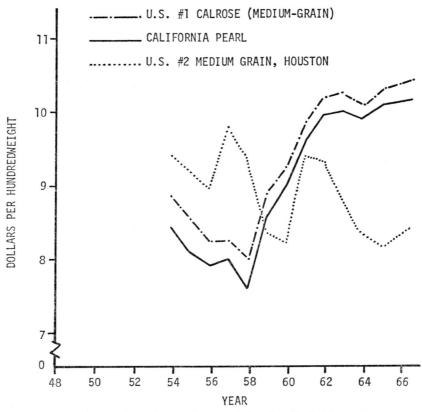

Figure 2-12. Milled Rice: Season Average Price for U. S. No. 1 Calrose and California Pearl, San Francisco or Stockton Docks, and U. S. No. 2 Medium Grains at Houston, 1954-66.

9.2 percent of the total. Meanwhile, medium-grain rice increased from 38.4 to 42.3 percent of total U. S. production. The loss of the Cuban export market in 1960-61, changes in support price levels and/or aggressive selling efforts by California could account for some of the divergence among prices by types and between California and the southern area.

Retail Prices

Retail prices reported by the Bureau of Labor Statistics for selected U. S. cities and the U. S. average show relatively little year-to-year variation. The index of retail rice prices increased rather steadily from around 100 in the mid-1950's to 107 in 1966. The all-food index rose about 20 points, the white bread index about 30 points. Potato prices were variable, being relatively high in 1964-66.

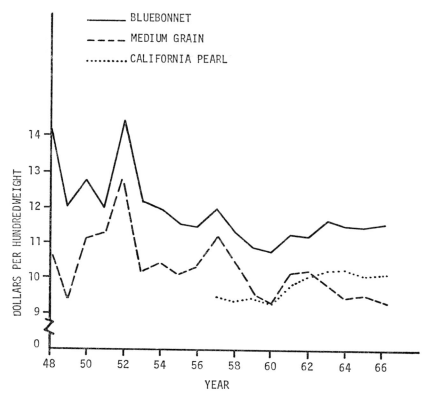

Figure 2-13. Milled Rice: Season Average Price by Variety, New York, 1948-66.

Retail rice prices exhibited a slight but steady increase during the 1958-67 decade with only minor year-to-year variations. Prices of foods presumed to compete with rice were relatively higher than rice prices based on the 1957-59 average. However, rice is such a small part of the average household food budget that its price elasticity of demand is probably quite low although it would vary over different income levels. Pratt reported a retail price elasticity of demand for rice of 0.5 at retail while Brandow suggests a farm price elasticity of demand (excluding exports and feed) at 0.037.[17,18] In summary, rice sales do not respond greatly to changes in price; however, rice prices do respond significantly to changes in the quantity available.

[17]Pratt, P. M., *Rice: Domestic Consumption in the United States,* Bureau of Business Research, Austin, The University of Texas Press, 1960.

[18]Brandow, G. E., *Interrelations Among Demands for Farm Products and Implications for Control of Market Supply,* Pennsylvania Agr. Exp. Station Bulletin 680, August 1961.

39

Retail prices for long-grain rice were 2-3 cents per pound above short-grain prices based on the U. S. averages.

TRENDS IN CONSUMPTION

An individual's consumption of a given food commodity presumably depends on its price relative to the prices of competing commodities, on his income and on his preferences for the commodity. The major factors which determine total world demand for rice are population and real income or buying power. Other things being equal—per capita buying power, relative prices, and tastes and preferences—world demand would vary at a 1:1 ratio with population changes. Besides population increases, net increases in real income per capita generally will increase total world demand for rice. Relative changes between rice prices and prices of competing cereals probably will not affect total world demand; however, such changes would tend to affect regional demands. Detailed treatment of the structure of world demand for rice has been prepared by FAO.[19,20]

Characteristics of World Demand[21]

Consumption patterns in developing countries are determined to a large extent by production patterns because of underdeveloped marketing systems. In the United States, rice producers and consumers are separate groups. This situation contrasts with the larger producing and consuming areas in Asia where high rice prices could stimulate a rise in on-farm consumption as a result of increased income from that portion sold. Some 50-70 percent of the world rice crop is under this type of "subsistence" production. Rice consuming areas, insofar as they can be separated from producing areas, are influenced by market factors such as incomes, prices, urbanization, consumer tastes and the special nature of rice as a meal rather than as a single food. The demand for rice is not homogeneous throughout the world, being ingrained in some countries, transitory in some and negligible in others.

The world's rice consumers may be separated into three types: habitual consumers, those in the process of changing from so called "inferior" foods such as millet or sorghum to rice or wheat and those in the bread eating regions who eat rice occasionally as a special dish or because of ease of preparation.

Most habitual consumers live in the Far East and account for the bulk of the world's consumption, Table 2-13. Their demand is

---

[19]United Nations, FAO, *The World Rice Economy, Volume II, Trends and Forces,* Commodity Bulletin Series 36, Rome 1966.

[20]United Nations, FAO, *The State of Food and Agriculture 1966,* Rome 1966.

[21]The following five sections on general characteristics are taken primarily from the FAO's situation and outlook statement for the International Rice Year 1966.

TABLE 2-13. MILLED RICE: RECENT TRENDS IN TOTAL, AND PER CAPITA CONSUMPTION (FOOD USES) IN RELATION TO POPULATION GROWTH, 1950-52 TO 1961-63

Country	Population growth 1951-62 Index 1951 = 100	Total rice consumption			Per capita rice consumption		
		1950-52 average	1961-63 average	1961-63 index 1950-52 = 100	1950-52 average	1961-63 average	1961-63 index 1950-52 = 100
		– – Million cwts. – –			– – Pounds – –		
Developing countries							
Far East							
Burma	124	50.49	70.11	139	269	302	112
Ceylon	130	15.87	23.57	148	203	231	114
China (Taiwan)	142	24.25	35.49	146	287	295	103
India	123	462.08	707.39	153	126	157	125
Indonesia	128	126.76	184.22	145	165	187	113
Philippines	135	40.56	57.52	142	187	196	105
Thailand	139	57.32	75.84	132	284	271	95
Africa and Near East							
W. Africa	136	7.72	15.43	200	42	62	147
Iran	123	5.07	9.79	193	31	49	157
Iraq	124	2.20	2.73	124	42	42	100
Saudi Arabia	133	.84	1.98	237	18	31	175
United Arab Republic	123	8.60	18.14	211	40	68	172
Latin America							
Argentina	139	1.76	1.96	111	11	9	80
Brazil	134	39.02	69.93	179	73	97	133
Peru	130	2.87	5.38	188	33	55	166
Venezuela	151	.88	1.52	172	18	20	113
Total developing countries[1]	128	1,107.97	1,646.84	149	132	152	115
Developed countries							
Japan	112	193.78	244.86	126	229	258	113
United States	120	8.13	12.26	151	4	7	126
W. Europe	107	19.20	23.48	122	6	7	114
Total developed countries[2]	112	221.12	280.60	127	40	46	114

[1]Included several other countries listed in source table.
[2]Countries listed only.
Source: United Nations, FAO, *The State of Food and Agriculture, 1966*, Rome, p. 147.

generally inelastic regarding changes in prices and income. Frequently, the consumer produces all that he eats. Rice constitutes the vast majority of their calorie intake.

Consumers in the process of changing diet patterns because of urbanization, income growth, or changes in relative prices do not have the well-defined preference of the habitual rice eater. Therefore, they can be influenced by changes in relative prices and income. This type of consumer may be found in West Africa and in parts of Latin America and Asia. Peru, Brazil, Saudi Arabia, United Arab Republic, Iran and West Africa all experienced rates of increase in per capita consumption above the average for the developing countries between 1950-52 and 1960-63, Table 2-13.

The demand for rice in the world's bread regions (Near East, North Africa, Europe and North America) is not affected greatly by economic factors. Although insignificant in terms of world consumption, these areas are important in world trade.

Among habitual rice eaters, strong preferences are exhibited for specific types of rice. Long-grain *Indica* rice, which separates freely when cooked, accounts for the bulk of the world demand and is strongly preferred by the mass of rice eaters in southern and southeastern Asia. Round or short-grain *Japonica* rices, which are soft-cooking varieties that cling together when cooked, are consumed mainly in Japan, China (Taiwan), Korea and parts of mainland China. Round-grain rice is consumed also in Mediterranean countries where grown.

The changes in rice production, population and production per capita in developing countries during 1949-65 are shown in Figure 2-14. Rice production per capita on a world-wide basis dropped to a decade low in 1967.

Population

Population growth is the predominant factor affecting world demand—essentially at a 1:1 ratio. In additon to sheer numbers, the changing rural-urban distribution of population may affect rice consumption per capita. Per capita rice consumption in urban areas in Japan was significantly below that in rural areas in 1960: 218 and 346 pounds, respectively. A similar pattern is evident in the Philippines and China (Taiwan). On the contrary, urbanization in eastern India and East Pakistan has stimulated the demand for rice and wheat, possibly because these areas are in an earlier stage of economic development.

Incomes

Given the predomination of rice in the diets of many developing countries coupled with the inadequate diet situation of many of

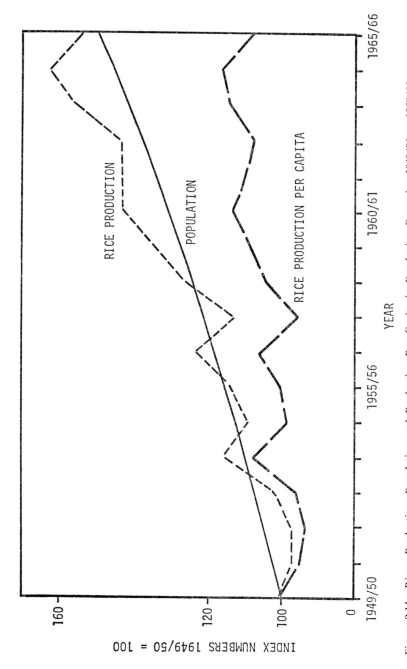

Figure 2-14. Rice: Production, Population and Production Per Capita in Developing Countries, 1949/50 to 1965/66.

Source: United Nations, FAO, *Commodity Review*, 1966, Rome, p. 53.

these countries, rising income may cause a significant increase in consumption per capita. Although rice consumption per capita does level off at some point, it seems unlikely that rice will become supplementary as bread and potatoes are in high income countries.

Income elasticities of demand[22] for rice are reported to vary from a high 0.6 in Indonesia to −0.1 in Japan. Rice consumption per capita seems to have reached its saturation point at 276-331 pounds in the traditionally exporting countries of the Far East (Burma, Cambodia, Thailand and the Republic of Vietnam) and Malaysia. Income elasticities for the Philippines have been estimated at 0.1 in rural areas and −0.1 in urban areas. China (Taiwan) is reported to have an income elasticity of only 0.06.

The strong preferences which may be expressed for different qualities of rice are reflected in the income elasticity coefficients for domestic and imported rice of 0.1 and −1.6, respectively, in Japan.

Change in Relative Prices

Estimates of price elasticities of demand[23] for rice are more difficult to obtain than income elasticities. However, price elasticities are probably very low among habitual rice consumers. Preference for the round-grain type is so strong that Japanese consumers prefer to supplement it with processed barley rather than switch to imported long or medium-grain rice with different cooking qualities.

Price Disparities and Consumer Subsidies

Economies of volume in production and marketing generally cause the most readily available staple food to be the lowest priced in the local market. Thus bread costs about twice as much as rice in the Far East, whereas the situation is reversed in the Near East and North Africa except for the United Arab Republic, an important rice producer.

The relationships among cereal prices in international markets are not necessarily reflected in retail prices due, for example, to high farm support prices (Japan), inflation (Indonesia and Republic of Korea) and subsidies (Ceylon). Japan, like Ceylon, subsidizes rice consumption heavily but its unusually high paddy support prices keep retail prices relatively high, Figure 2-15.

Nearly all major rice importing countries control the volume of their imports in attempts to isolate their domestic markets and prices from international developments. In importing countries expensive

---

[22]Defined as the percent change in consumption associated with a 1.0 percent increase in income with prices constant.

[23]Defined as the percent change in quantity purchased with a 1.0 percent change in price with income and related prices held constant.

44

rice (excluding subsidized rice) may reflect high domestic costs of production (Africa) or guaranteed producer prices (Latin America).

Competition with Other Foods

Changes in relative prices and price disparities appear to have no significant effect on world rice consumption. The traditonal popularity of rice in the Far East, of bread in North Africa and the Near East, of maize tortillas in Central America and of gari (cassava) in West Africa probably will not be affected appreciably by year-to-year price changes among these products. Food habits and general living customs are too strong.

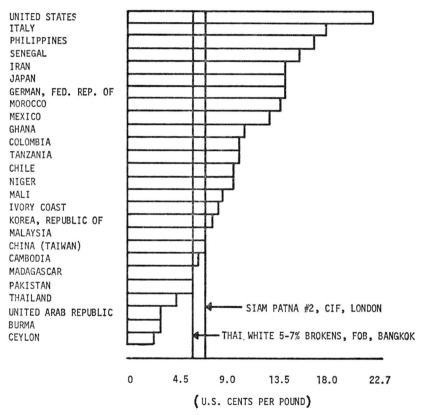

Figure 2-15. Domestic Retail Prices of Rice in June 1965, Compared with Average International Prices in 1965.

Source: United Nations, FAO, *The State of Food and Agriculture* 1966, Rome, p. 150.

45

Rice competes with wheat in China (mainland), parts of central India, Korea, West Pakistan and most of the Near East; with maize in Cambodia, Indonesia and the Philippines; with beans, maize and starchy roots in Latin America; and with millet, sorghums and starchy roots in West Africa. However, established consumer preferences for rice place it in a good competitive position relative to other cereals. Moreover, the tropics are better suited for the production of rice rather than wheat which has to be imported.

Rice consumption is expected to expand as incomes increase in many areas of the Far East, West Africa and Latin America. This expansion will be at the expense of other cereals such as barley and millets as well as beans and starchy roots in some areas. The demand for rice appears to be saturated in only a few areas: Burma, Thailand, Republic of Vietnam, Cambodia, China (Taiwan) and Japan. Wheat is considered unlikely to effect a permanent change on the world demand for rice in the foreseeable future.

Feed and Industrial Utilization

More than 90 percent of the world's rice is consumed as human food. Use for animal feed, in brewing and nonfood manufacturing always has been small and is smaller today (1963) than before World War II.[24] In terms of absolute volume, Japan, United States, Philippines, Republic of Vietnam and India were the largest nonfood consumers of rice in 1958-59. Industrially, alcoholic preparations are the predominant nonfood outlet for rice other than for feed (India).

Unless rice supplies increase unexpectedly and make rice relatively cheap, nonfood use probably will remain low.

U. S. Rice Consumption

Per capita

Contrary to trends for most cereal products and related substitutes between 1950 and 1964, per capita consumption for rice increased 14 percent in the 48 states during the same period.[25] Overall, per capita rice consumption in the United States increased by more than 40 percent between 1950 and 1967, Table 2-14. Part of this increase reflected results of reporting on a 50-state basis after 1960 (Hawaii added about one-third pound to the U. S. average) and of USDA donation programs which have averaged about 10 percent of total consumption since 1957.

---

[24]United Nations, FAO, *The World Rice Economy, Volume II, Trends and Forces,* Commodity Bulletin Series 36, Rome 1966.

[25]Hiemstra, S. J., "Consumption and Prices of Cereal and Bakery Products," *National Food Situation,* ERS NFS 112, May 1965.

The increase in rice consumption was due largely to increased use in breakfast cereals—increasing from 1.3 million hundredweight in the mid-1950's to nearly 2.0 million hundredweight in the early 1960's.[26] Rice used in soups has increased some during the last decade, but canned rice and rice in baby foods has trended generally downward.

Rice consumption varies significantly among regions and among income groups. The 1955 Household Food Consumption Survey showed that families with an annual income of less than $2,000 consumed nearly three times as much rice per person as did families in the $6,000-$8,000 income group. However, rice consumption, based on both percentage of households using and quantity per household, increased as annual income exceeded $10,000, thus exhibiting a U-shaped distribution over income.[27] Consumption patterns by income

[26]Askew, W. R., "U. S. Rice Utilization," *Rice Situation*, ERS RS 11, January 1967.
[27]U. S. Department of Agriculture, *Food Consumption of Households in the United States*, Household Food Consumption Survey 1955, Reports 1-5, December 1956.

TABLE 2-14. PER CAPITA CONSUMPTION OF RICE AND SELECTED COMPETING FOODS IN U.S., 1948-67

	Civilian consumption per capita			
	Rice milled	Wheat flour[1]	Cornmeal and hominy	Potatoes[2]
	— — — — — Pounds per capita — — — — —			
1948	4.9	137	15.6	105
1949	5.0	136	15.4	110
1950	5.1	135	14.4	106
1951	5.8	133	13.4	114
1952	5.3	131	12.9	102
1953	5.4	128	12.2	108
1954	5.3	126	11.7	107
1955	5.5	123	11.2	109
1956	5.8	121	11.1	103
1957	5.7	119	10.8	109
1958	5.4	121	10.6	105
1959	5.0	120	10.5	107
1960	6.1	118	10.1	108
1961	6.2	118	10.0	109
1962	7.4	115	10.0	107
1963	6.6	113	9.9	111
1964	7.0	114	9.8	110
1965	7.6	113	10.4	108
1966	7.3	111		113
1967	7.3	112		115

[1]Includes white, whole wheat, semolina and durum flour.
[2]Farm weight, fresh equivalents.
Source: USDA, *U.S. Food Consumption, Sources of Data and Trends*, 1909-63, Stat. Bull. 364, June 1965 and supplements thereto.

groups may have changed significantly since 1955, but preliminary 1965 survey data suggest such is not the case.

In 1955, rice consumption per household in the South was four times as great as that in the North Central region, almost three times that of the Northeast and more than twice that in the West. The South was the largest consumer in all income groups with the regional disparities leveling out in the $8,000-$9,999 income per household category. The heterogeneous distribution of rice consumption is supported also by Eiland's study of rice distribution in 1966-67 which, for example, indicated that Louisiana's per capita consumption was about five times the U. S. average and 15 times that in the W.N. Central and New England Mountain regions, Table 2-15.[28]

Total Utilization

U. S. rice is used domestically as food, both commercial and donation, and in industry, mostly in brewing, Table 2-16. USDA donations accounted for roughly 10 percent of the total civilian food disappearance during 1956-65.

Brewery use of rice amounted to 8.6 and 6.2 percent of the total milled rice supply during 1956-58 and 1964-66, respectively. Brewery use dropped to a low of 2,767 thousand hundredweight in 1963 but rose to 3,819 thousand hundredweight in 1966. Much of the imported rice is broken rice used by breweries.[29]

---

[28]McGrath, E. J., *Distribution Patterns of Rice in the United States*, U. S. Department of Agriculture, ERS 186, July 1964.

[29]Askew, W. R., "U. S. Rice Utilization," *Rice Situation*, ERS RS 11, January 1967.

TABLE 2-15. DISTRIBUTION OF MILLED RICE FOR DIRECT FOOD USE, SELECTED STATES AND AREAS, U.S., 1966-67

State or territory	Milled rice for direct food use, 1966-67:	
	Proportion of U.S. total	Per capita
	Percent	Pounds
United States		5.7
California	12.5	7.4
Hawaii	4.5	73.5
Puerto Rico		128.9
Louisiana	10.7	32.6
New York	13.1	7.9
South Carolina	4.4	19.1
Texas	6.2	6.5
W.N. and Central and N. England	5.8	2.6 or less

Source: J. C. Eiland, *Distribution of Rice in the United States, 1966-67*, ERS-408, USDA, Washington, D. C., April 1969.

TABLE 2-16. MILLED RICE: U.S. DISAPPEARANCE AS FOOD, 1956-66

| Year beginning August[3] | Civilian use[1] | | | | | | Territorial use[2] | Military procurement[4] | Total | Used by breweries |
| | USDA donations[2] | | | | Commercial | Total | | | | |
	Schools	Institutions	Needy	Total						
						1,000 cwt.				
1956	219	108	476	803	8,790	9,593	3,871	80	13,544	3,549
1957	198	87	563	848	8,282	9,130	3,960	135	13,225	3,348
1958	200	120	808	1,128	7,558	8,686	4,231	183	13,100	3,278
					Beginning 50-state basis					
1959	212	93	695	1,000	9,849	10,849	3,630	90	14,569	3,488
1960	219	84	864	1,167	9,986	11,153	2,835	127	14,115	3,482
1961	222	81	1,110	1,413	12,013	13,426	2,551	160	16,137	3,361
1962	219	74	943	1,236	10,973	12,209	2,970	117	15,296	2,911
1963	250	89	1,016	1,355	11,893	13,248	2,798	112	16,158	2,767
1964	256	97	951	1,304	13,214	14,518	2,820	154	17,492	3,095
1965	307	91	807	1,205	12,863	14,068	2,752	82	16,902	3,391
1966	306	90	667	1,063	13,194	14,257	2,764	100	17,121	3,819

[1]Rice consumed by continental U.S. civilians, including that consumed by the military eating from civilian food supplies.
[2]Include approximately 300,000 cwt. shipped annually to the territories and Puerto Rico under the donation program.
[3]USDA donations are on a year beginning July.
[4]Procured by the military for military use at home and abroad.
Source: USDA, *Rice Situation*, ERS, RS-12, January 1968, p. 13.

Broadly, the distribution of U. S. milled rice among domestic food outlets during 1964-66 was 76.2 percent commercial sales, 6.9 percent USDA donations, 16.2 percent shipments to the territories and 0.7 percent military procurement for military use at home and abroad. USDA donations were 8.3 percent of total domestic civilian food use during 1964-66.

3

Production and Consumption Projections -- 1975 and 1980

Warren R. Grant
Carl E. Shafer

PROJECTED PRODUCTION

Projections of world rice production for 1975 and 1980 were based on yield and acreage trends that were evident during 1948 through 1966 with allowances for anticipated changes in trends. Where the trends in the 1960's deviated from this over-all period, adjustments were made in the projected production to reflect the effects of current conditions. The 1966 allotment level of 2.0 million acres was assumed for the United States for the projected dates.[1] Relative prices were assumed at the same level as in the late 1960's. It was assumed that the conflict in Southeast Asia would be settled before the 1975 projection period. In addition, no major disturbances (man or weather) were anticipated for the projection periods.

World Projections

World rice production increased 69 percent between 1948 and 1967. This increase was due to gains in both yield and acreage, with yields improving annually at an average of 1.9 percent and acreages increasing annually at an average of 1.5 percent. Total world production, 5.9 billion hundredweight in 1967, is expected to continue increasing through the two projection periods at about the same average annual rate as in 1948-66, Figure 3-1. The world production projected in this study for 1975 of 7.4 billion hundredweight is similar to that projected by the Food and Agricultural Organization of the United Nations.[2] The projected production for 1980 of 8.1 billion hundredweight is 8 percent less than the projection in the *World Food Problem*, Table 3-1.[3] No projections for 1980 were made by the United Nations. The projections in the *World Food Problem* for

---

[1]The 20 percent increase in allotments for 1968 would increase the projected production level. However, production would not be expected to increase the full 20 percent because of the use of marginal land and the spreading of limited resources over a larger acreage.

[2]United Nations, FAO, *Agricultural Commodities—Projections for 1975 and 1985*, Vol. I, Rome, 1967.

[3]President's Science Advisory Committee, *The World Food Problem*, Report of the Panel on World Food Supply, Vol. II, The White House, May 1967.

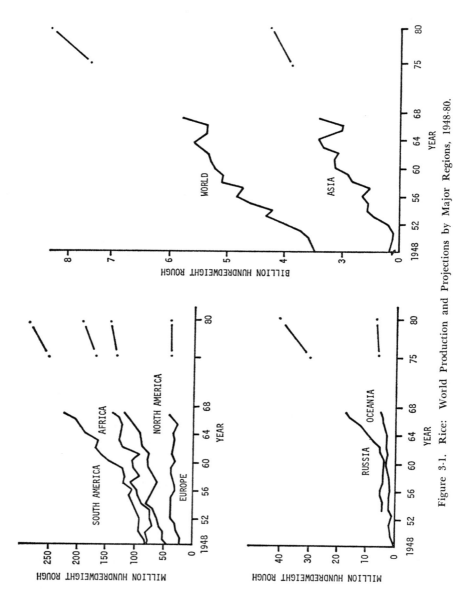

Figure 3-1. Rice: World Production and Projections by Major Regions, 1948-80.

52

TABLE 3-1. RICE: PROJECTED PRODUCTION FOR 1975 AND 1980

| Area | 1964-66 average | Rice market study projections | | World food problem | | FAO 1975[1] | |
		1975	1980	1970[2]	1980[2]	Assumption I	Assumption II
				Million cwt.			
Major region							
North America	100.97	133.23	146.46	121.39	146.97	140.21	125.00
South America	192.97	250.63	285.37	223.80	280.59	253.55	272.16
Africa	127.83	169.60	193.08	158.06	216.12	176.04	196.54
Oceania	4.40	6.18	7.16	4.68	6.68	5.11	5.34
Europe	32.70	39.44	40.95	38.25	44.09	44.20	48.77
Russia	12.87	30.38	40.18	26.72	33.40	18.25	26.46
Asia	3,165.17	3,919.00	4,258.00	3,681.01	5,027.16	4,123.42	4,463.57
Region total	3,636.91	4,548.46	4,971.20	4,253.91	5,755.01	4,760.12	5,137.84
World	5,485.90	7,372.00	8,055.00	6,725.73	8,761.28	7,333.14	7,775.20
Major exporting countries							
Burma	175.73	215.24	238.18			211.44	242.51
Thailand	225.38	281.20	292.20			262.35	271.17
United States	78.16	106.42	118.81	92.99	102.55	94.91	68.34
Italy	12.80	16.75	17.39			15.10	15.10
United Arab Republic	43.62	59.00	67.00			64.70	64.70
Major importing countries							
India	1,095.88	1,422.00	1,512.00			1,703.55	1,793.74
Ceylon	21.96	30.10	34.10			36.74	46.76
Japan	354.53	400.95	425.25			417.54	394.16
Philippines	89.87	108.00	117.00			96.87	146.97
Indonesia	307.16	375.00	400.00			330.69	377.45
Republic of Vietnam	106.44	150.00	175.00			140.29	163.67

[1] Assumption I assumes a gross domestic product growth at or slightly below past trends. Assumption II assumes a gross domestic product growth commensurate with national economic plans.
[2] Converted to rough rice at 66 percent conversion rate.

53

1980 anticipate a rapid adoption of research results from the International Rice Research Institute.

Recent research results have been applied successfully in several areas.[4, 5] These results are based on a combination of input changes such as new varieties, heavy fertilization, control of insects and weeds, control of flooding and a dependable water supply. All of these changes require additional capital and knowledge. According to Brown, not more than one-third of Asia's land is suitable for the new, short-stemmed rice varieties because of either too little or too much water.[6] It appears doubtful, therefore, that known technology will be fully adopted on all acreage by 1980. Trends before 1967 did not indicate any major improvements in yields in the Far East. However, preliminary estimates of the 1968 world crop indicate a 16 percent increase in world production over the drouth years of 1965-66. Much of this increase can be attributed to improved growing conditions. New technology has made major contributions to improvements in yields in a few areas of the world. World yields are projected to increase to about 2,270 pounds per acre by 1980, a 23 percent increase over the 1964 world yield of 1,847 pounds per acre, Figure 3-2.

World rice acreage is expected to increase through 1980 at a slightly lower rate than occurred during 1948-64, approaching 355 million acres by 1980. This would be a 16 percent increase over the 306 million acres harvested in 1964, Figure 3-3.

Regional Projections

Asia, the world's dominant rice-producing region, is not expected to maintain as high a rate of growth in production between 1964-66 and 1980 as that experienced between 1948 and 1964. Additional acreage in this region is limited, leaving little room for expanding production through acreage increases. Acreage harvested in Asia in 1965 and in 1966 was off slightly from the peak acreage of 1964. Acreage for this region was projected to be 228.9 million acres for 1980, a 12 percent increase over the 1964-66 period, Figure 3-3. The greatest potential for expanding production is through yields which averaged only 1,430 pounds per acre between 1948 and 1966. Research by the International Rice Research Institute in the Philippines is anticipated to have some impact on yields. However, this effect may be dampened by the facts that more than 50 percent of the rice produced in this region is not irrigated and that no more than one-third of Asia's land is suitable for the new, short-stemmed rice varieties.

Yields are expected to increase to about 1,860 pounds per acre by 1980, a 20 percent increase over the 1964-66 average annual yield,

[4]"Breakthrough Against Hunger: 'Miracle' Rice for Far East," *U. S. News and World Report,* December 4, 1967, pp. 68-69.
[5]Brown, Lester R., "Agricultural Revolution in Asia," *Foreign Affairs,* July 1968.
[6]*Ibid,* p. 696.

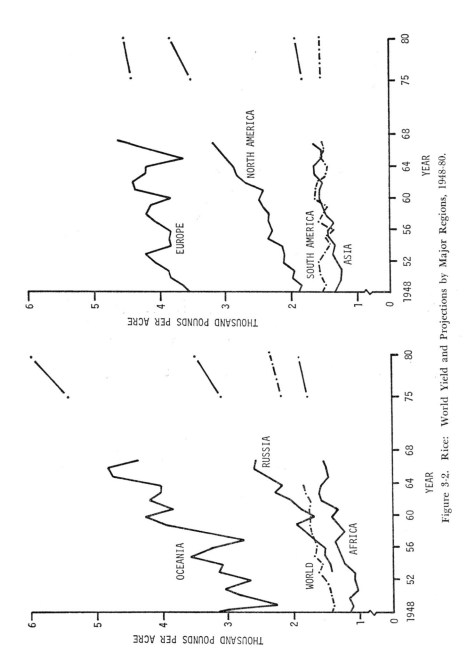

Figure 3-2. Rice: World Yield and Projections by Major Regions, 1948-80.

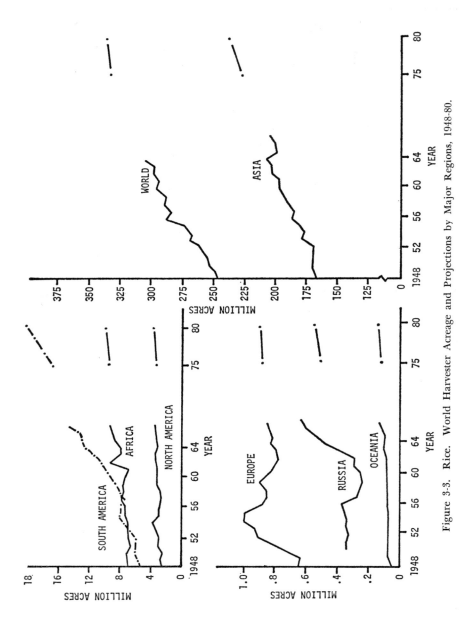

Figure 3-3. Rice. World Harvester Acreage and Projections by Major Regions, 1948-80.

Figure 3-2. Production in this region is projected to be 4.3 billion hundredweight for 1980, a 35 percent increase over the average 3.2 billion hundredweight produced annually between 1964-66.

During this study important questions have arisen regarding the potential rate of increase in rice production in Asia. Significant gains in production were reported in 1968 and projected for 1969, with India in particular experiencing large increases. These gains were due to a combination of weather, technology and increased inputs, and the future seems brighter due to the promise of the latter two factors. How widespread the effect of these factors will be remains to be seen. The authors of this chapter believe that the projections presented herein are realistic in terms of the allowances made for improved technology and increased inputs as they will be adapted in Asia.

In North and Central America, production is expected to increase 45 percent from the 1964-66 average annual production to 146 million hundredweight by 1980 primarily because of yield increases, Table 3-1. Yields are expected to continue the sharp trend upward to slightly less than 4,000 pounds by 1980, about 34 percent above the average annual yields during 1964-66, Figure 3-2. Acreage in the United States, the major producer in the region, was assumed constant at the 1966 allotment level of 2.0 million acres for both projection periods. Acreage in Mexico and other Central American countries should increase slightly during the projection period, Figure 3-3.

Rice production in South America increased 182 percent during 1948-67. This rise in production is due almost entirely to acreage increases, since yields have remained relatively constant during the period. There are still large areas in South America which could be developed for rice production.[7] The projected production increases for this region are based on a continued expansion of acreage. Acreage is expected to reach 18.3 million acres by 1980, a 43 percent increase over the 1964-66 average annual acreage, Figure 3-3. Yields are low, have not improved much during the past 18 years and are not expected to improve much over the projection periods, Figure 3-2. The projected production for 1980 at 285.4 million hundredweight is about 48 percent above the 193 million hundredweight average annual production during 1964-66, Table 3-1.

African production has risen 76 percent since 1948, due about equally to both yield and acreage increases. The projected production for the region, 193.1 million hundredweight for 1980, reflects a continuation of the yield and acreage increases. Africa, like South America, is a region in which large areas could be developed for rice production.[8] Anticipating an expansion of the areas, rice acreage

---

[7]United Nations, FAO, *Agricultural Commodities—Projections for 1970,* Rome, 1962.
[8]*Ibid.*

is expected to increase by 18 percent from the 1964-66 average annual acreage to 10 million acres by 1980 and yields by 28 percent to almost 2,000 pounds per acre, Figures 3-2 and 3-3.

Government programs have restricted production somewhat below full capacity at present prices in Europe. However, rice production, relatively stable during 1948-67, is expected to rise slightly during the projection periods (40.9 million hundredweight by 1980). These projections reflect slight increases in yields and acreage. Russian production has increased rapidly since 1960 due to both an expansion in acreage and an improvement in yields. This rate of growth is expected to continue during the projection periods. Oceania, with an average annual rate of increase in production of 11.4 percent during 1948-67, had the largest rate of increase. This trend is expected to continue during the projection periods. However, this region produced less than one-tenth of a percent of the world production in 1967.

Major Exporting Country Projections

In the major exporting countries production is expected to continue upward during the projection periods, Table 3-1. In Burma, production peaked at 187.6 million hundredweight in 1964 followed by yield and acreage declines in 1965, 1966 and 1967 resulting in considerably lower production, Figure 3-4. Burma's policy of nationalization of the rice industry has disrupted the rice economy of that country.[9] Assuming that the "disruption" can be settled before 1975, Burma's production should be slightly above the 1964 level. The anticipated increase above this level for 1980 is based largely on yield improvements rather than acreage expansions. Thailand's production increased sharply in 1966 with an additional 2 million acres harvested, Figure 3-4. However, drouth lowered the 1967 crop about 16 percent from the 1966 level. Rice was harvested from 17.0 million acres in 1966 while cultivated land totaled only about 22 million acres in 1962.[10] Thus, any major increase in production will need to come from yield increases. Improved production practices are not generally applicable on the large flood plains where controlled irrigation is not possible.[11]

The projections for the United States assume the 1967 allotment of 2.0 million acres with the increases due to yield improvements. By 1980, yields in the United States should approach 6,000 pounds per acre, a 42 percent increase over the average 1964-66 annual yields, Figure 3-4. Government policy is a major factor in determining U. S.

[9]U. S. Department of Agriculture, *The Far East and Oceania Agricultural Situation —Midyear Review*, ERS-Foreign 197, September, 1967.

[10]Chugg, Boyd A., *Agriculture in the Southeast Asian Rice Bowl and Its Relation to U. S. Farm Exports*, USDA, ERS, Foreign Agr. Econ. Rep. No. 26, 1965.

[11]Ellis, Leonard B., "Trends in World Rice Production and Trade," paper presented at Rice Technical Working Group, Little Rock, Arkansas, June, 1966.

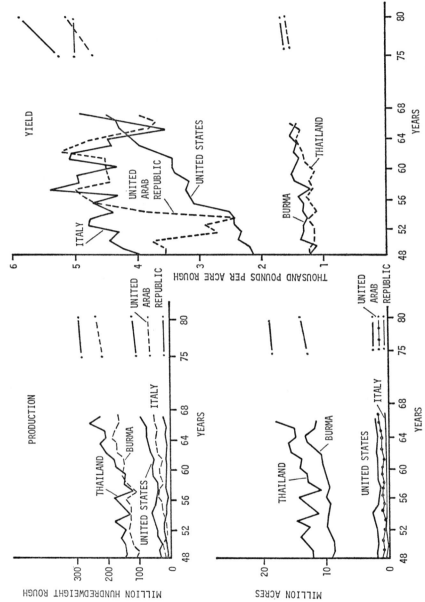

Figure 3-4. Rice: Yield, Production and Acres with Projections of Major Exporting Countries, 1948-80.

production. With no acreage controls, rice acreage could increase considerably above the 1967 level. Recent research indicates that about 8.5 million acres are suited to rice production in the southern rice areas.[12] However, water and rotation restrictions would limit this land to a maximum of 3.6 million acres of rice in any given year. In Italy production has remained relatively stable the last 10 years. Little change in production, yield or acreage is expected through the projection period. Production in the United Arab Republic remained at about 44 million hundredweight during 1962-66. Increases in acreage were offset by lower yields. The projected production reflects yields increasing slightly by 1975 and 1980, Figure 3-4. The area available for rice has almost reached its peak. Completion of the Aswan Dam will add little land suitable for rice cultivation, but the adequate supply of irrigation water together with some improvement in cultural practices should result in increased yields.[13]

Major Importing Country Projections

The major importing countries are expected to show some improvements in production during the projection period. Production projections for these countries are in Table 3-1 and Figure 3-5. India, the second largest producer in the world, has a long history of being deficit in rice. Recent government programs have attempted to overcome this deficit and some progress has been made. Unfavorable weather conditions cut production drastically in India in 1965 and 1966, but production increased by one-third in 1968 because of weather, technological improvements and increased inputs. The projected production is based largely on expected yield improvements. The fourth Five Year Plan, 1966-71, calls for a compound rate of growth of 5.6 percent in agricultural production.[14] This is in line with the country's growing needs, but it appears ambitious for rice production, considering past achievements. Ceylon has made efforts to increase rice production through fertilizer and planting subsidies and through improved irrigation facilities. Progress has been made, but the projected production is not expected to offset population growth. Japan's harvested acreage has remained relatively stable at about 8 million acres since 1956. The acreage should remain at about this level through the projection period. The increases in production will result from yield improvements.

[12]Mullins, Troy; Grant, W. R.; Campbell, J. R.; Gerlow, A. R.; Bonnen, C. A.; and Welsch, D. E.; *Resource Use Adjustments in Southern Rice Areas, Part I: Effects of Price Changes with Unrestricted Rice Acreages*, Ag. Expt. Sta. of Ark., La., Miss., and Texas and USDA, Southern Coop. Ser. Bul. 122, 1967.

[13]Ellis, Leonard B., "Trends in World Rice Production and Trade," paper presented at Rice Technical Working Group, Little Rock, Arkansas, June 1966.

[14]U. S. Department of Agriculture, *The Far East and Oceania Agricultural Situation*, ERS-Foreign 188, 1967.

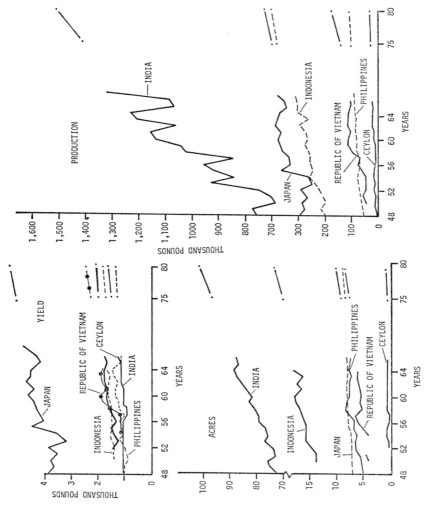

Figure 3-5. Rice: Yield, Production and Acres with Projections of Major Importing Countries, 1948-80.

61

Yields in the Philippines rank among the lowest of any of the major rice producing countries. A small improvement occurred during the 1960's. However, yields will have to undergo rapid improvement in the projection period in order for this country to be self-sufficient in her rice needs. The International Rice Research Institute, located in the Philippines, should influence production. Such significant production gains were made in the Philippines in 1968 that the Philippines were self-sufficient for the first time since 1903. However, the continued growth of production is anticipated to be slow.

Indonesia, the major rice importing country of the world in the early 1960's, is moving closer to satisfying its rice needs. A concentrated attack on low rice yields by the government has resulted in production increasing from 259 million hundredweight in 1963 to 315 million hundredweight in 1967.

Under peaceful conditions, the Republic of Vietnam would be a rice exporter. Under existing conditions, this nation is a major importer. This switch from surplus to deficit puts a heavy drain on world export suppliers.[15] This situation is expected to be reversed before the 1975 and 1980 projection periods in that a settlement of the Vietnam War is expected.

PROJECTED CONSUMPTION

World rice consumption in 1975 and 1980 will, of necessity, be equivalent to world production for those years, plus or minus carry-over stocks. Ideally, the production-consumption projections for these years would be derived through a comprehensive model of the world rice economy which would allow for variation in not only population and incomes (buying power) but relative prices as well. However, as with many projections, those herein were derived from past trends in yields and acreage, adjusted by current conditions, on the production side and assumed population and income changes, adjusted by income elasticities, on the consumption side. Hence, the production and consumption projections are independent and the resulting "deficits" must be resolved either through (a) changes in relative prices with higher prices for rice, (b) government aid programs external to the market or (c) a combination of these.

Recent projections for world rice consumption for 1975, 1980 and 1985 are available. Projections for rice consumption have been made by both the Food and Agriculture Organization of the United Nations and the U. S. Department of Agriculture. FAO's most recent projections are those for 1975 and 1985 issued in October of 1966[16]

---

[15]Ellis, Leonard B., "Trends in World Rice Production and Trade," paper presented at Rice Technical Working Group, Little Rock, Arkansas, June 1966.

[16]FAO issued revised Volumes I and II of the 1975 and 1985 projections in 1967 which contained little or no change for rice. United Nations, FAO, *Agricultural Commodities—Projections for 1975 and 1985*, Vol. I & II.

while *The World Food Problem,* a report of the President's Science Advisory Committee published in May of 1967, contains 1970 and 1980 projections prepared by the USDA.[17] The amount of material available in these reports on both world and country by country projections is impressive and these sources were utilized in developing the consumption projections for rice in this study.

Current and Nearby Situation

The 1967-68 world crop (rough) was 11.0 percent greater than the 1966-67 crop and larger than the big 1964-65 crop of about 5,600 million hundredweight. World demand was expected to continue strong in 1967-68 as production has been increasing at a lower rate than population in the major rice importing countries, and Thailand's crop was expected to be about 15 percent below that of 1966-67. World exports of rice for calendar year 1967 may approximate the 6.9 million tons traded in 1966. [18, 19] Rice production in 1967-68 reached record highs in India, Pakistan, Japan, the Philippines and the United States. In particular, India's 1967-68 rice production increased by about 34 percent above the two previous poor years and 6 percent above the previous high for India. A combination of favorable weather, increased use of fertilizer and high-yielding varieties are believed responsible for India's record production.

United States exports in 1967-68 exceeded the record 37.8 million hundredweight (milled) of the previous season because most of the increase in world production occurred in India which needs all of its production for domestic consumption.

Longtime Projections

World rice production-population trends were favorable for increased rice consumption per capita from 1950 to 1963 with per capita rice consumption rising 15 and 14 percent in the developing and developed countries, respectively: total world rice consumption was increasing by 49 and 27 percent, respectively.[20] However, between 1963 and 1966, world per capita consumption of rice was rather stable, declining in 1965-66 due to bad weather in the Far East. Limited growth in exportable supplies of rice partly reflects lack of strong price incentives due to the fact that the larger part of the world's rice is under direct government-to-government contracts or official control of some type. Even though rice prices increased during 1967-68, exportable supplies will remain limited.

[17]President's Science Advisory Committee, *The World Food Problem,* Report of the Panel on World Food Supply, Vol. II, The White House, May 1967.

[18]U. S. Department of Agriculture, *The World Agricultural Situation,* (Outlook 1968), ERS-Foreign Agr. Econ. Rep. 38, February 1968.

[19]U. S. Department of Agriculture, *Rice Situation,* ERS, RS 12, January 1968.

[20]United Nations, FAO, *The State of Food and Agriculture 1966,* Rome, 1966.

Some perspective on the world rice situation may be gained by comparing the world population and production projections in *The World Food Problem,* Table 3-2. Assuming that world population in 1980 will be about 145 percent of 1959-61, world per capita consumption could presumably be maintained with a commensurate growth in world rice production; *i.e.,* 45 percent. This would provide for no improvement in presently existing inadequate diets in some regions. However, the projections in *The World Food Problem* suggest rice supplies will be 166 percent of 1959-61 or 14 percent higher than projected population in 1980. The higher projected consumption in 1980 versus 1959-61 reflects, of course, increased economic, as well as population, growth.

The 1980 projections of *The World Food Problem* report suggest a reversal of the tight rice supply situation which they projected for 1970. They assume that (a) the adoption of new rice varieties developed at the International Rice Research Institute in the Philippines, (b) the return of Vietnam as a net exporter subsequent to a successful termination of the war and (c) the continuation of mainland China as a rice exporter will result in abundant supplies and lower world prices for rice relative to other grains.

TABLE 3-2. WORLD POPULATION PROJECTIONS AND DOMESTIC DIS-APPEARANCE OF RICE COMPARED, 1959-61 AVERAGE AND 1965, 1970 AND 1980

	Period				
	1959-61	1965	1970	1975	1980
World population Millions					
High			3,624	4,005	4,467
	3,011.5	3,308			
Low			3,599	3,911	4,264
Percent of 59-61					
High			120.3	133.0	148.3
	100.0	109.8			
Low			119.5	129.9	141.6
World domestic dis-appearance of rice Total (million cwt. rough)	5,276.3	5,929.7	6,725.73		8,761.27
Percent of 59-61	100.0	112.4	127.5		166.0
Developed countries	100.0	111.0	116.2		148.7
Developing countries	100.0	112.5	128.6		167.7

Source: Population from *The World Food Problem,* Vol. II, p. 90. Domestic disappearance from pp. 164 and 171.

The FAO 1975 projections are based on alternative Gross Domestic Product growth rates.[21] According to past trends in yield, acres, and policies, FAO projected world rice production at 7,388.8 million hundredweight (rough)[22] by 1975 under their low Gross Domestic Product (GDP) assumptions, including 2,428 million hundredweight for mainland China; or an overall average rate of growth of production of 2.5 percent per year, Table 3-3. FAO projected world rice demand for 1975 (low GDP) is very similar at 7,415.5 million hundredweight (rough), about 0.4 percent in excess of projected production; *i.e.*, supplies and demand remain more or less in balance. World population was expected to grow at the rates shown in Table 3-4.

Although world production-consumption is shown in-balance in 1975, the developing countries' deficit is 73.5 million hundredweight, up from essentially a balanced situation during 1961-63. This suggests a sharp increase in the net export deficit, largely in the Far East and to a lesser extent in Latin America and Africa, Table 3-3. These higher import needs could amount to a total of about 300.6 million hundredweight in 1975 which could be met by the exporting countries, particularly the United States.[23] This projected increase in trade of between 67 to possibly 100 million hundredweight for 1975 would be shared between round-grain rice and long-grain rice. This assumes that increased rice deficits will not be met with other cereals which is reasonable in light of the consumer preferences in the countries involved. Export prices might rise to $150 to $160 per ton versus $120 in 1961-63. Here, it should be noted that world total indigenous exports *were* already 249.5 million hundredweight in 1965 or 20.2 percent greater than during the 1961-63 period.[24] World exports dropped to 234 million hundredweight in 1966 while world imports jumped about 12 percent being about 20 percent above the 1961-63 period. Thailand's rice price (f.o.b. Bangkok) rose 42 percent between July 1966 and June 1967.

Under FAO's high GDP assumption, projected world demand at constant prices would be 7,629.3 million hundredweight in 1975, only 2.9 percent greater than projected under the low GDP assumption, Table 3-4. Most of the increase would come in the developing coun-

---

[21]For the world as a whole, the low and high growth rates of GDP were assumed to be 3.7 and 5.1 percent, respectively, for the 1965-75 decade and 3.6 and 5.3 percent, respectively, for the 1975-85 decade. United Nations, FAO, *Agricultural Commodities—Projections for 1975 and 1985*, Rome, 1967, p. 9.

[22]All metric ton milled equivalent figures have been converted to million hundredweight rough rice in text.

[23]The 300 million hundredweight of rough rice is approximately the same as that obtained by extrapolation of the 1950-65 trend in world exports to 1975; FAO, *The State of Food and Agriculture 1966*, p. 185.

[24]United Nations, FAO, *Monthly Bulletin of Agricultural Economics and Statistics*, 15 (12), December, 1966.

TABLE 3-3. RICE: PRODUCTION, TOTAL CONSUMPTION (ALL USES) AND BALANCES, 1961-63 AND PROJECTIONS TO 1975

Regions and countries	1961-63 average			1975					
				Low GDP assumption			High GDP assumption		
	Production	Consumption	Trade	Production	Demand	Balance	Production	Demand	Balance
	Million cwt., rough equivalent								
Developing countries	2,979.6	2,959.5*	(—)	4,195.4	4,268.9	73.5	4,626.4	4,432.6	— 193.7
Far East exporters	638	481*	133.6	828.4	668.1	— 160.3	915.2	688.1	— 227.1
Burma	163.7	110.2	53.4	217.1	150.3	— 66.8	250.5	157.0	— 93.5
Cambodia	53.4	40.1*	10.0	76.8	56.8	— 20.0	86.8	60.1	— 26.7
China (Taiwan)	60.1	56.8	3.3	80.2	76.8	— 3.3	86.8	73.5	— 13.4
Thailand	203.8	140.3*	50.1	263.9	203.8	— 60.1	270.6	207.1	— 63.5
Vietnam Republic	110.2	106.9	3.3	140.3	137.0	— 3.3	163.7	143.6	— 20.0
Far East importers[1]	2,007.5	2,117.8*	110.2	2,865.0	3,069.7	204.7	3,136.5	3,190.0	53.4
Ceylon	23.3	40.1*	16.7	36.7	63.5	26.7	46.8	66.8	20.0
India	1,155.7	1,172.4	16.7	1,703.6	1,703.6	(—)	1,793.7	1,767.0	— 26.7
Indonesia	263.8	297.3	33.4	330.7	404.2	73.5	377.5	420.9	43.4
Malaysia	23.3	43.4	20	30.1	63.5	33.4	33.4	63.5	30.1
Pakistan	364.1	364.1	(—)	537.8	524.4	— 13.4	581.2	537.8	— 43.4
Philippines	86.8	90.2	3.3	96.9	153.7	56.8	147.0	160.3	13.4
Latin America	190.4	197.1*	6.7	283.9	297.3	13.4	330.7	307.3	— 23.4
Brazil	130.3	130.3	(—)	197.1	197.1	(—)	227.1	207.1	— 20.0
Africa	76.8	93.5*	16.7	110.2	130.3	20.0	130.3	140.3	10.0
Near East	66.8	66.8*	(—)	106.9	103.5	— 3.3	117.0	106.9	— 10.0
U.A.R.	40.1	30.1*	10	66.8	46.8	— 20.0	66.8	50.1	— 16.7
Developed countries	491	481*	23.4	564.4	537.8	— 26.7	517.7	531.1	13.4
North America	66.8	26.7*	40.1	100.2	36.7	— 63.5	70.1	33.4	— 36.7
W. and S. Europe	36.7	46.8*	10	40.1	56.8	16.7	43.4	60.1	16.7
Japan	387.5	404.2*	6.7	417.5	437.6	20.0	394.2	430.9	36.7
Centrally planned countries	1,924	1,917.3*	3.3	2,628.8	2,608.8	— 20.0	2,702.3	2,665.6	— 36.7
Eastern Europe and U.S.S.R.	10.0	26.7*	16.7	23.4	33.4	10.0	30.1	33.4	3.3
China (mainland)	1,783.7	1,763.7	20	2,428.4	2,401.7	— 26.7	2,485.2	2,451.8	— 33.4
World total	5,394.6	5,357.8*	26.7	7,388.8	7,415.5	26.7	7,846.4	7,629.3	— 217.1

(—) Less than 3.3 million cwt.

*Including changes in stocks.

[1]Countries with net trade deficit in all cereals in 1961-63, though Pakistan and Korea export rice. Excludes Japan.

Source: United Nations, FAO, *Agricultural Commodities—Projections for 1975 and 1985*, Vol. I, Rome, 1967, p. 106 (Table 4 figures

TABLE 3-4. WORLD POPULATION GROWTH: FAO ASSUMPTIONS

Areas	Population 1965		Past and assumed rates of growth				Population 1985[2]	
	Million	Percent of world total	1950-62	1965-75	1975-85[1]	1975-85[2]	Million	Percent of world total
			—	Percent per year compound		—		
Developed countries	727	21	1.3	1.1	0.8	1.1	906	18
North America	214	6	1.7	1.4	1.1	1.5	288	6
West and South Europe	378	11	1.0	0.9	0.5	0.8	444	9
Other developed countries	135	4	1.5	1.3	1.0	1.3	174	3
Centrally planned countries	1,128	34	2.0	1.8	1.1	1.8	1,605	32
U.S.S.R. and Eastern Europe	333	10	1.5	1.1	0.9	1.1	415	8
Asian centrally planned countries	795	24	2.3	2.0	1.2	2.1	1,190	24
Developing countries	1,500	45	2.3	2.6	2.1	2.5	2,473	50
Latin America	244	7	2.6	2.8	2.2	2.7	422	9
Africa	249	8	2.4	2.6	2.3	2.7	415	8
Near East	111	3	2.3	2.7	2.2	2.7	190	4
Asia and Far East	896	27	2.1	2.5	1.7	2.3	1,446	29
India	483	14	2.0	2.4	1.9	2.2	755	15
World total	3,355	100	2.0	2.0	1.6	2.0	4,984	100

[1]Low population assumption (U.N. low variant).
[2]High population assumption (U.N. medium variant). For more detail see Tables I.1 and I.2 in the Statistical Appendix, Mullins, Troy; Grant, W. R.; Campbell, J. R.; Gerlow, A. R.; Bonnen, C. A.; and Welsch, D. E., *Resource Use Adjustments In Southern Rice Areas*, Part I: *Effects of Price Changes with Unrestricted Rice Acreages*, Southern Coop. Ser. Bul. 122, Ag. Exp. Sta. of Ark., La., Miss, and Texas and USDA, 1967.
Source: United Nations, FAO, *Agricultural Commodities—Projections for 1975 and 1985*, Vol. I, Rome, 1967, p. 7.

tries where the income elasticity is declining but still positive. Production would have to show a greater increase to be consistent with the higher GDP's in the major producing countries. The 7,846.4 million hundredweight (rough) production projected for 1975 would be 2.8 percent (217.1 million hundredweight [rough]) greater than the projected demand. National development plans would have simultaneously raised exportable supplies and reduced deficits. Production in the developed areas would also rise faster than demand. The aggregate deficit of importing countries would be similar to the 200 million hundredweight actual imports in 1961-63. Overall, a decline in prices would be necessary to avoid an excess of export supplies with the main burden of adjustment probably falling on the non-traditional exporters of Latin America. The FAO 1975 projections for the United States (North America) reflects a cutback in rice acreage due to the lack of prospect for trade in long-grain rice. Hence, FAO's North America high GDP production projection is 30 percent below that of the low GDP projection, Table 3-3.

On the whole, the FAO 1985 demand projections suggest a massive increase in world requirements for rice over the next 15 years—an additional 3,290 million hundredweight per year by 1985 divided 70:30 between the developing and developed nations, Table 3-5.[25] This figure could be reduced by 10 percent if population growth is held to the lower rate in Table 3-4. FAO suggests that in lieu of this supply forthcoming, a change in the composition of diets might be induced but would require a significant alteration in the agricultural production patterns of major rice producing counties.

Consumption Projections for Rice Marketing Study

In the projection process, assumptions regarding the future obviously affect the level of the projection. The usual economic environment assumptions are: normal weather, no worldwide military conflict, stable price relationships, some rate of economic growth, and a continuation of current policies and programs affecting agriculture and trade in both foreign countries and the United States. Generally, alternative assumptions are made regarding economic growth and population change resulting in alternative projections for the same period. The effect of alternative assumptions is illustrated by the FAO 1975 projections which yield a range of 27 million hundredweight (rough) world import deficit to 217 million hundredweight surplus due to low and high GDP assumptions, respectively, Table 3-3.

Procedure

Only one consumption projection was made for each year—1975 and 1980—for the rice marketing study. These projections were

[25]United Nations, FAO, *Agricultural Commodities-Projections for 1975 and 1985*, Vol. I, Rome, 1967.

TABLE 3-5. RICE: TOTAL AND PER CAPITA CONSUMPTION (AS FOOD) 1961-63 AND DEMAND PROJECTIONS TO 1985

Regions and countries	1961-63 average		Per capita demand (1985)				Total demand (1985)			
	Per capita	Total	Low GDP High population	High GDP High population	Low GDP Low population	High GDP Low population	Low GDP High population	High GDP High population	Low GDP Low population	High GDP Low population
	Pounds	Million cwt.	Pounds				Million cwt., rough equivalent			
Developing countries	127.9	2,702.3	136.7	141.1	136.7	141.1	5,090.6	5,304.4	4,970.4	5,147.4
Far East exports										
Burma	293.2	103.5	295.4	293.2	297.6	293.2	173.7	173.7	170.4	167.0
Cambodia	328.5	30.1	328.5	328.5	328.5	328.5	56.8	56.8	53.4	53.4
China (Taiwan)	291.0	50.1	291.0	269.0	288.8	266.8	86.8	80.2	80.2	73.5
Thailand	271.2	113.6	282.2	284.4	282.2	284.4	223.8	227.1	217.1	220.5
Vietnam Republic	370.4	83.5	381.4	392.4	383.6	390.2	133.6	140.3	133.6	133.6
Far East importers[1]										
Ceylon	242.5	36.7	255.7	273.4	264.6	273.4	80.2	86.8	76.8	76.8
India	158.7	1,085.6	176.4	183.0	176.4	183.0	2,017.5	2,104.4	1,980.8	2,054.3
Indonesia	187.4	280.6	189.6	218.3	191.8	218.3	494.4	567.9	491.0	554.5
Malaysia	264.6	40.1	271.2	262.3	271.2	260.1	83.5	80.2	83.5	80.2
Pakistan	207.2	327.3	222.7	220.5	222.7	220.5	618.0	611.3	601.3	594.6
Philippines	196.2	86.8	207.2	218.3	209.4	218.3	310.4	220.5	207.1	213.8
Latin America	52.9	180.4	55.1	59.5	57.3	59.5	360.8	377.5	344.1	357.4
Brazil	105.8	120.3	112.4	116.8	112.4	116.8	237.2	247.2	227.1	233.8
Africa	24.3	86.8	26.5	28.7	26.5	30.9	163.7	187.1	160.3	183.7
Near East	41.9	63.5	46.3	48.5	46.3	48.5	130.3	137.0	126.9	130.3
U.A.R.	70.5	30.1	75.0	77.2	77.2	77.2	60.1	63.5	60.1	60.1
Developed countries	41.9	437.6	37.5	37.5	37.5	37.5	521.1	521.1	507.7	507.7
North America	6.6	20.0	6.6	6.6	6.6	6.6	30.1	33.4	30.1	30.1
W. and S. Europe	6.6	40.1	8.8	8.8	8.8	8.8	56.8	60.1	56.8	60.1
Japan	255.7	370.8	240.3	238.1	240.3	238.1	427.6	420.9	417.5	410.9
Centrally planned countries	110.2	1,790.4	125.7	127.9	125.7	125.7	3,079.8	3,116.5	2,852.6	2,859.3
E. Europe and U.S.S.R.	4.4	23.4	6.6	6.6	6.6	6.6	40.1	40.1	36.7	36.7
China (mainland)	152.1	1,650.1	163.1	165.3	165.3	165.3	2,815.9	2,872.7	2,628.8	2,632.2
World total	103.6	4,930.3	114.6	119.0	114.6	116.8	8,691.5	8,942.0	8,330.7	8,514.4

[1]Countries with net trade deficit in all cereals in 1961-63, though Pakistan and Korea export rice. Excludes Japan.
Source: United Nations, FAO, Agricultural Commodities—Projections for 1975 and 1985, Vol. I, Rome, 1967, p. 111.

derived by interpolating the FAO projections assuming (a) the U.N. medium variant population level (Series B) and (b) an average of the low and high GDP rates used by FAO.[26] Specifically, the 1975 projection is the average of the FAO's high and low GDP projections, Table 3-3, while the 1980 projection is an interpolation of the 1975 and 1985 projections, Table 3-5.[27]

The Projections

The projected world rice production and consumption figures in Table 3-6 suggest an increasing deficit through 1980; i.e., projected demand based on population and economic growth outruns projected production based on past trends by 2.0 and 5.1 percent in 1975 and 1980, respectively, Figure 3-6. About 40 percent of the difference between the 1980 production-consumption projections would be eliminated if the low population series was used.

---

[26]The low GDP assumption is at or slightly below past trends. The high GDP assumption was commensurate with national economic plans, higher in the developing than the developed countries.

[27]Given the total rice demand projected by FAO for 1975 and 1985; i.e., combining population growth at the U.N. medium variant and average GDP growth, the compound rate of growth in total projected rice demand can be obtained with the following general formula: $Y_n = ar^{n-1}$

where: Y_n = value of total rice demand in nth year,

n = the number of the year relative to the base period,

r = annual rate of increase in total rice demand,

a = rice demand in base year.

In logs: $\log Y_n = \log a + n-1 (\log r)$

or to find r: $\log r = \dfrac{\log y_n - \log a}{n-1}$

TABLE 3-6. COMPARISON OF PROJECTED WORLD RICE (ROUGH) PRODUCTION AND CONSUMPTION FOR 1975 AND 1980

Projection	Year		
	1964-66	1975	1980
	— — — — — Million cwt. — — — — —		
Production[1]	5,486	7,372.00	8,055.00
Consumption			
Total		7,522.4	8,490.4
			(8,298.5)[2]
Food only		6,958.2	7,853.6
Deficit			
Total		150.4	435.4
			(243.5)[2]
Percent of consumption		2.0	5.1
			(2.9)[2]

[1]From Table 2-1, section on production projections.

[2]For low population projection, only one population figure is projected for 1975.

70

Under the assumptions used herein, the world situation continues to be rather tight through 1975 and particularly in 1980 in that the production projections are more conservative than those of other studies; i.e., the FAO average 1975 projected production level would be 7,617.5 million hundredweight (rough equivalent) (average of the 1975 production projections shown in Table 2-3) or 3-3 percent greater than the projections made in this study, Table 3-6. An important question is, how much will yields and, hence, production change in the developing countries in the next 12 years? The FAO International Rice Study Group reported that current trends suggest a growing gap between the supply and the demand for rice in developing importing countries unless steps are taken to increase the expansion of production.[28]

In contrast, two years later, Brown implies that past trends are no longer relevant to the food situation in Asia. He states that "As

[28]United Nations, FAO, *Monthly Bulletin of Agricultural Economics and Statistics*, 15 (12), December 1966.

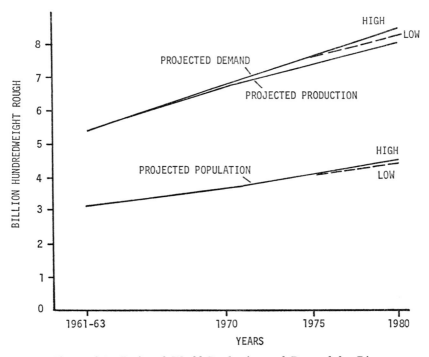

Figures 3-6. Projected World Production and Demand for Rice.

of mid-1968, both the food situation and the food production prospects in Asia have changed almost beyond belief."[29] Thus, as with any projection process, the results depend upon the assumptions regarding future growth rates. If, in fact, Asia is able to revolutionize their agriculture the deficits projected in Table 3-6 may become surpluses. However, the projected world rice production increase of 47 percent during the 15 years 1965 to 1980 does not seem inordinately conservative at the present.

It is, of course, conceptually possible that total demand might "exceed" total production by the amounts shown in Table 3-6. However, it would not be expected that total projected economic demand could far exceed supply in that a significant share of the increased GDP upon which the demand is based would have to be derived from rice production in developing counties. The type of deficit projected for 1975 and 1980 will be resolved through (a) higher prices for rice, (b) government-to-government aid programs external to the market or (c) a combination of these.

Projection by Major Exporting and Importing Countries

Projected "surpluses" and "deficits" for the major exporting and importing countries, respectively, appear in Tables 3-7 and 3-8. These are economic surpluses and deficits in the sense that demand based on population and income growth at stable prices is simply subtracted from the expected production for each country. These deficits are not net trade projections but do indicate the relative directions and magnitudes of trade expected. For example, India's economic demand for rice relative to its production is expected to increase during the projection period, Table 3-8. For the countries in Tables 3-7 and 3-8 only, and excluding mainland China, the 1961-63 "balance" was 74.1 million hundredweight "surplus" while the "deficits" for 1975 and 1980 were 240.0 and 416.8 million hundredweight (rough), respectively. Again, whether actual economic deficits of this magnitude can develop depends upon the economic growth of the developing countries. If GDP's do rise as assumed, the deficits would be reflected in higher prices which might in turn precipitate increased production. Note that Vietnam returns as a net exporter in 1975 and 1980, Table 3-8.

The Philippines, shown here as an importing country, reported a record crop in 1967-68 which permitted them to export some rice in 1968. Again, the rate at which the potential for yield increasing varieties and practices is fulfilled is crucial to the validity of the projections herein.

---

[29]L. R. Brown, "The Agricultural Revolution in Asia," *Foreign Affairs*, July 1968, pp. 688-698.

TABLE 3-7. MAJOR EXPORTING COUNTRIES: 1961-63 BALANCE AND 1975 AND 1980 PROJECTED PRODUCTION AND CONSUMPTION FOR ROUGH RICE

Major exporting countries	Period		
	1961-63 balance	1975	1980
	— — — — — Million cwt. rough — — — — —		
Burma			
Production	160.58	215.24	238.18
Consumption	108.48[1]	153.70	169.90
Difference	52.10[2]	61.54	68.28
Thailand			
Production	202.85	281.20	292.20
Consumption	139.82	205.40	223.70
Difference	63.03	75.80	68.50
United States			
Production	63.49	106.42	118.81
Consumption	25.28	33.90	36.70
Difference	38.21	72.52	82.11
China (mainland)			
Production	1,756.40		
Consumption	1,736.10	2,426.70	2,732.00
Difference	20.30		
Italy			
Production	14.15	16.75	17.39
Consumption	9.98	11.10	11.60
Difference	4.17	5.65	5.79
United Arab Republic			
Production	39.68	59.00	67.00
Consumption	29.99	48.20	56.70
Difference	9.69	10.80	10.30

[1]Converted at individual rates.
[2]Difference between production and consumption; not necessarily equal to net exports in United Nations, FAO, *Agricultural Commodities—Projections for 1975 and 1985,* Vol. I, Rome, 1967, p. 113.

CONCLUDING REMARKS

The world rice situation is, of course, but part of the total world food problem. Although the climate for economic development in Asia seems markedly improved over two years ago, it is difficult to be overly optimistic regarding the world's food situation between now and 1985.[30,31] Massive increases in world food needs are projected through 1985. The needs may be fulfilled through a combination

---

[30]West, Quentin M., *Major Forces Affecting the World Food Situation,* ERS, USDA, paper presented at the National Agricultural Policy Conference, Tahlequah, Okla., September 11, 1968, p. 21.

[31]President's Science Advisory Committee, *The World Food Problem,* Report of the Panel on the World Food Supply, Vol. I, the White House, May 1967.

TABLE 3-8. MAJOR IMPORTING COUNTRIES: 1961-63 BALANCE AND 1975 AND 1980 PROJECTED PRODUCTION AND CONSUMPTION FOR ROUGH RICE

Major importing countries	Period		
	1961-63 balance	1975	1980
	— — — — — Million cwt. rough — — — — —		
India			
Production	1,142.09	1,422.00	1,512.00
Consumption	1,171.10[1]	1,734.80	1,966.05
Difference	−29.01[2]	−312.80	−454.05
Ceylon			
Production	21.60	30.10	34.10
Consumption	39.60	63.70	75.40
Difference	−18.00	−33.60	−41.30
Japan			
Production	376.48	400.95	425.25
Consumption	402.60	435.30	450.45
Difference	−26.12	−34.35	−25.20
Philippines			
Production	86.13	108.00	117.00
Consumption	91.20	157.20	190.86
Difference	−5.07	−49.20	−73.86
Indonesia			
Production	275.66	375.00	400.00
Consumption	296.90	412.30	480.16
Difference	−21.24	−37.30	−80.16
Republic of Vietnam			
Production	111.24	150.00	175.00
Consumption	104.90	140.50	152.26
Difference	6.34	9.50	22.74

[1]Converted at individual rates.
[2]Difference between production and consumption; not necessarily equal to net imports in United Nations, FAO, *Agricultural Commodities—Projections for 1975 and 1985*, Vol. I, Rome, 1967, p. 113.

of economic growth in the developing countries and capital and technical aid from the developed countries. The projected deficits between world production and consumption for 1975 and 1980 are a product of both population and economic growth. Population growth alone represents the sheer need, largely in developing countries, for rice and other foodstuffs. Population growth plus projected economic growth represents effective or economic demand. If the developing countries experience the projected rates of economic growth, it appears that effective demand for rice will expand significantly. However, the human need based on population growth will exist apart from the ability to mobilize economic demand.

4

An Examination
Of Policy Framework
For the Rice Industry

Marshall R. Godwin
Lonnie L. Jones
Troy Mullins
Fred H. Tyner
William R. Morrison

CURRENT PROGRAM

Conditions Leading to Its Implementation

Evidence of the intention of Congress to support the prices of agricultural commodities was contained in the Agricultural Adjustment Act of 1938, with the declared policy to assist "farmers to obtain, in so far as practicable, parity prices for such commodities and parity of income, and . . . consumers to obtain an adequate and steady supply of such commodities at fair prices." The objectives of U. S. agricultural legislation in general are also stated in the 1948 Act providing a Federal Charter for the Commodity Credit Corporation (CCC) as: "for the purpose of stabilizing, supporting, and protecting farm income and prices, of assisting in the maintenance of balanced and adequate supplies of agricultural commodities . . . and of facilitating the orderly distribution of agricultural commodities."

Other more recent Acts of Congress indicate that the objectives of income maintenance and the adjustment of supplies to needs are the most important goals with respect to the production and marketing of rice.

Prior to World War II, U. S. rice production was less than 25 million hundredweight and, for 7 years after the war ended, there was a great scarcity of rice and a corresponding rise in prices. This situation resulted from wartime and postwar disruptions which reduced production and export availabilities in important rice producing countries.

In 1952, the world rice situation began to change as export supplies became more abundant. Unusually favorable growing conditions and expanded rice acreage, both in importing and exporting countries, helped to bring about this increase. By the fall of 1953, prices of rice in world trade began to move downward from record levels reached in 1952-53. The difference between the world price and the higher U. S. support price required that the CCC acquire large stocks of rice in the next several years.

While carryover stocks as of August 1953 amounted to only 1.5 million hundredweight, the large 1953 crop left a carryover in August 1954 of over 7.5 million hundredweight. Another large crop in 1954 built the 1955 ending stocks up to 26.7 million hundredweight. In view of these heavy accumulations, acreage allotments and marketing quotas were proclaimed for the 1955 rice crop. Quotas became effective following a referendum in which over 90 percent of rice farmers voted in favor of quotas. With the second largest crop of record produced in 1955, the carryover jumped to 34.6 million hundredweight on August 1, 1956. Marketing quotas were again proclaimed for the 1956 crop following a favorable vote of 84.6 percent of the rice farmers. Marketing quotas have been approved by farmers each year since that time.

Prior to the 1961 crop, the Secretary was required to proclaim marketing quotas for rice for the coming crop year whenever the total supply for the preceding marketing year exceeded the normal supply by more than 10 percent. In subsequent years the law provides for marketing quotas if the total supply for the preceding marketing year exceeded the normal supply, that is, the 10 percent above normal supply margin was dropped.

If quotas are approved by two-thirds of rice farmers voting in a referendum, producers remaining within their acreage allotments will be eligible for price support on their entire production. If marketing quotas are disapproved, no restrictions are placed on rice marketings. Acreage allotments, however, remain in effect as a condition of eligibility for price support at 50 percent of parity as required by law when quotas are disapproved.

Historical Price Support Methods

Producer prices for rice have been directly supported by loans, purchase agreements and purchases since 1948. Loans are non-recourse, meaning that delivery of rice on which the loan was obtained constitutes payment of the loan in full regardless of the current market value of the rice. Purchase agreements, which have now been discontinued for rice, allowed producers to sell up to an agreed-upon amount of rice to CCC at the support price. Purchases by CCC commodity offices also serve to support the market price of rice.

Indirect support has been extended through a program of export subsidies to allow U. S. rice to compete in the world market. When the U. S. support price for rice exceeds the world price, subsidy payments to exporters allow U. S. rice to be sold at the world price, thus broadening the rice market and indirectly supporting the domestic price.

When rice supplies are larger than anticipated needs, the law requires that efforts be made to limit production through acreage allotments and marketing quotas. Under acreage allotments, producers are assigned specified acreages which they cannot exceed if they wish to be eligible for price support. Marketing quotas—if approved by two-thirds of the producers voting in a referendum—impose marketing penalties on any producer who exceeds his allotted acreage.

Principal Features of Program

Current rice legislation is encompassed in the Food and Agriculture Act of 1965. The rice program is designed to maintain income of rice growers and at the same time keep production in line with demand.

The 1965 Act relates to the crops of 1966, 1967, 1968 and 1969, and provides for a minimum rice allotment of 1,818,638 acres (the 1965 allotment) through these years. Marketing quotas are to be proclaimed by the Secretary if total supply exceeds normal supply and if quotas are approved by producers voting in a referendum. Definitions of these "supply" terms are given in the sections that follow dealing with acreage allotments and marketing quotas.

Acreage Allotments

Acreage allotments have been in effect since 1955 and are designed to maintain supplies in accordance with anticipated demand. The Secretary is required to announce an acreage allotment for rice for each year. Unless suspended by the Secretary to meet a national emergency, farm acreage allotments are in effect each year. If a marketing quota program is not in effect, compliance with the rice acreage allotment is required for price support eligibility. When a marketing quota program is in effect, compliance with the acreage allotment is required to avoid the assessment of a marketing quota penalty as well as price support eligibility.

The national acreage allotment for rice is computed on the basis of a legislative formula very similar to the marketing quota determination. The law states that the allotment for any year "shall be that acreage which the Secretary determines will, on the basis of the national average yield of rice for the five calendar years immediately preceding the calendar year for which such national average yield is determined, produce an amount of rice adequate, together with the estimated carryover from the marketing year commencing in such calendar year not less than the normal supply . . . ."

To illustrate the full meaning of the law, a schematic representation of the allotment determination for the 1968 crop year follows.

First, it is necessary to determine the normal supply of rice. This consists of three elements:

1. Estimated domestic consumption during the period August 1, 1967 - July 31, 1968

2. Estimated exports for the year beginning August 1, 1968

3. An allowance for carryover consisting of 10 percent of the estimated domestic consumption and exports.

The sum of the three foregoing amounts constitutes the basis for determining the production needed in 1968. The production needed consists of the normal supply less the estimated carryover of rice anticipated as of August 1, 1968. Once needed production is established, the national acreage allotment is determined by dividing this quantity of rice involved by the national average yield of rice per planted acre during the preceding 5 years (in this case 1963-67). The national acreage allotment is divided among producers based on past acreages of rice, allotments previously established and other factors, such as abnormal conditions affecting acreage, availability of land, labor and equipment, crop rotation practices and type of soil. In Arkansas, Mississippi and Southwest Louisiana, the allotment is made on a farm basis, and the allotment is the farm's share of the national allotment. In other major areas, allotments are established on a producer basis, and a producer who permanently withdraws from rice production may transfer his rice acreage history to another producer. The recipient of this transferred history must plant at least 90 percent of his total producer allotment for at least 3 out of the next 4 years in order for the transfer to become permanent.

Table 4-1 shows data relating to rice production, carryover and price and indicates the national allotment for 1955-65. The allotment by states for 1956-67 is shown in Table 4-2.

Marketing Quotas

Marketing quotas must be announced by the Secretary if total supply at the end of a marketing year is equal to or exceeds the normal supply for the upcoming market year. The quotas, after approval of two-thirds of rice producers voting in a referendum, are then in effect for rice produced in the following crop year. The procedure for determining normal supply of rice for marketing quota purposes is the same as that discussed previously for determining acreage allotments. Total supply for any marketing year is defined as carryover for that marketing year, plus the estimated U. S. production during the calendar year in which the marketing year begins.

The rice marketing year is defined to be the period beginning on August 1 and ending the following July 31. Assuming that we

TABLE 4-1. DATA RELATING TO RICE SITUATION AND GOVERNMENT PROGRAMS FOR RICE, 1948-65[1]

Year beginning August 1	Production	Carryover[2]	Support	Season average price received by farmers	National allotment
	— — 1,000 cwt. — —		— Dollars per cwt. —		Acres
1948	38,320	2,505	4.08	4.88	
1949	40,787	3,469	3.96	4.10	
1950	38,840	4,519	4.56	5.09	
1951	46,122	2,040	5.00	4.82	
1952	48,278	1,515	5.04	5.87	
1953	52,924	7,546	4.84	5.19	
1954	64,254	26,700	4.92	4.57	
1955	55,969	34,618	4.66	4.81	1,928,334
1956	49,503	20,103	4.57	4.86	1,652,596
1957	42,954	18,169	4.72	5.11	1,652,596
1958	44,775	15,669	4.48	4.68	1,652,596
1959	53,669	12,144	4.38	4.59	1,652,596
1960	54,591	10,080	4.42	4.55	1,652,596
1961	54,198	5,334	4.71	5.14	1,652,596
1962	66,045	7,730	4.71	5.04	1,817,856
1963	70,269	7,539	4.71	5.01	1,818,166
1964	73,166	7,677	4.71	4.90	1,818,166
1965	76,281	8,234	4.50	4.93	1,818,638

[1]Source: *Rice Situation,* January 1967 and previous issues.
[2]Ending stocks as of July 31 of the next year.

wish to determine the relationship between total and normal supply for the 1968 crop of rice, the foregoing definitions translate into formula terms as follows:

Normal supply:
Estimated domestic consumption
(August 1, 1966 - July 31, 1967)
+ Estimated exports (August 1, 1967 - July 31, 1968)
+ Required carryover (10 percent of sum of the above)

Total supply:
Carryover (as of August 1, 1967)
+ Estimated production (during calendar year 1967)
+ Estimated imports (August 1, 1967 - July 31, 1968)

If total supply as calculated above does not exceed normal supply, then the Secretary cannot proclaim marketing quotas. Thus, there are no penalties imposed for rice production exceeding the acreage allotment. However, only rice produced on the acreage allotted is eligible for price support in this case.

TABLE 4-2. RICE: ACREAGE ALLOTMENTS, BY STATES, 1956-67[1]

State	Year								
	1956	1957	1958	1959	1960 and 1961	1962	1963, 1964 and 1965	1966	1967
					Acres				
Arizona	229	299	299	299	299	252	252	277	252
Arkansas	399,084	398,890	399,014	398,855	399,012	438,920	439,019	482,921	439,019
California	299,820	299,674	299,767	299,648	299,766	329,748	329,822	362,804	329,822
Florida	957	956	957	956	957	1,052	1,053	1,158	1,053
Illinois	20	20	20	20	20	22	22	24	22
Louisiana	475,094	474,863	475,010	474,821	475,008	522,517	522,635	574,899	522,635
Mississippi	46,683	46,660	46,675	46,656	46,674	51,343	51,354	56,489	51,354
Missouri	4,580	4,578	4,767	4,765	4,767	5,244	5,245	5,770	5,245
North Carolina	29	29	29	38	38	42	42	46	42
Oklahoma	149	149	149	149	149	164	164	180	164
South Carolina	2,847	2,846	2,846	2,845	2,846	3,131	3,132	3,445	3,132
Tennessee	517	517	517	517	517	569	569	626	569
Texas	422,390	422,185	422,316	422,147	422,313	464,522	464,657	511,123	464,657

[1]Source: *Rice Situation*, January 1967 and previous issues.

Price Support

Producer prices for rice are supported through loans and purchases designed to maintain prices at not less than a specified national average level. For the 1967 rice crop, the national average support price is required to be at least 65 percent of parity as of August 1, 1967. Support levels (percent of parity) for recent years as of the beginning of the marketing year were:

Year	Percent of parity
1966	67
1965	69
1964	74
1963	73
1962	76

Producers must be in compliance with acreage allotments to be eligible for price support. Support is extended through non-recourse loans and through purchases. Non-recourse loans allow delivery of the rice to constitute full payment of the loan regardless of the current market value of the rice. Purchase agreements which formerly were used as a means of price support for rice have been discontinued. Producers now can sell any or all of their eligible rice to the CCC, exclusive of any amount needed as loan collateral, and they may sell after the maturity date of loans.

Rice must be stored in approved farm or commercial facilities to be eligible for price support loans. This price support is available to all eligible producers on their eligible rice production from harvest-time through January 31 of the following year. To obtain price support the producer must file a timely application with the county ASCS office. Where a loan is obtained on warehouse-stored rice, the producer is required to surrender the warehouse receipt covering such rice. On-farm stored rice is inspected and the storage facility sealed by an inspector from the county ASCS office.

A cooperative marketing association can obtain price support for its members' rice, providing it meets the eligibility requirements in regulations issued by the CCC. The association must request approval to participate in the price support program by August 1 of the applicable calendar year or by such later date as the Executive Vice President, CCC, may authorize to alleviate hardship. This request must include submission of an application and completed questionnaire to the State Agriculture Stabilization Conservation Committee.

The maturity date for rice loans is April 30. Loans can be redeemed at any time prior to maturity by repayment of the principal amount plus charges (mainly 30 cents per $100 per month). If loans are not repaid, the rice pledged as security is taken over by the government at maturity, and a service charge of one cent per hundredweight is made on each hundredweight delivered.

CAPABILITY OF CURRENT U. S. POLICY TO COPE WITH PROJECTED CONDITIONS OF THE FUTURE

Administrative Latitude for Program Formulation

The 1965 Food and Agriculture Act provided the basic framework for a 4-year rice program. Within this general framework, the Secretary of Agriculture is afforded considerable latitude in formulating program regulations for a specific year. This latitude pertains to both the level of acreage allotment and the level of price support but relates primarily to raising these levels, since minimums are written into the law.

Most actions by the Secretary have been concerned with efforts to reduce burdensome surpluses and the need to provide support to prices at the farm level. Present legislation specifies the conditions under which certain actions to control total production can be taken. When these conditions are not present, the Secretary has no authority to impose marketing quotas. Consequently, by not granting authority for action on the part of the Secretary, the legislation determines the kind of program that can be operative when the situation shifts from one of controlled output to that of fostering expanded output.

With respect to probable quantity requirements, the three following fairly distinct situations can be visualized in which the requirement may be for an increase in the size of the annual rice crop.

1. For needed production levels that can be attained with the current production base, the Secretary can announce that marketing quotas are in effect and increase allotments, thus encouraging the planting of a larger total average on present rice farms. This course of action is open to the Secretary only if total supply during a marketing year exceeds estimated normal supply.

2. For a comparatively large upward adjustment in annual production, it is reasonable to expect that estimated normal supply would be greater than the total supply of rice. Under these conditions the Secretary would have no authority to impose marketing quotas.

With quotas suspended the Secretary may still announce an allotment, in which case new producers could plant and market rice without being penalized, but they would not earn history for allotment eligibility in later years. The level of acreage allotments to old growers would be a discretionary matter which could be increased by the Secretary if such action were deemed desirable.

3. For a market upward adjustment in annual production, both an increase in the production base and incentives to growers to increase rice acreages might be necessary. Under such conditions the Secretary could suspend acreage allotments and marketing quotas. In this situation both current and new growers would be eligible for any price support loans made available to growers, and total acreages grown could be used in establishing allotments in subsequent years. These features would serve as strong incentives for new growers in some areas to bring additional land into production.

In making a judgment concerning adequacy of present legislation to allow the Secretary to keep annual supplies reasonably well in line with projected needs, one must take into account the probable magnitude of the change in requirements that may occur within short periods. If only modest changes in requirements are anticipated the normal increase in yields, combined with comparatively small changes in acreage allotments, likely would permit annual production to be adjusted reasonably close to requirements. For the most part this position assumes that the present production base is adequate to meet modest changes in requirements and through changes in acreage allotments the problem of supply management could be effectively accomplished.

Alternative projections of rice production using the existing resource base under the present allotment program are shown in Figure 4-1. If we assume that the 1948-66 average annual yield increase of 127 pounds per acre is sustained through the period being considered then the present allotment of 2.0 million acres would result in a U. S. crop in 1980 of about 118 million hundred pounds, or about 30 percent above the 1967 level of output.[1] However, this average yield increase likely would be hard to maintain for the duration of this period. If an annual yield increase of 80 percent of the average for the 1948-66 period is used, U. S. production in 1980 would stand at about 114 million hundred pounds with no relaxation in allotments. This projection also reflects rather optimistic yield increases.

Should a U. S. crop of 125 to 130 million hundred pounds be needed in the 1980 period, no doubt some relaxation of allotments would be necessary. A 10 percent increase in the allotment to 2.2 million acres coupled with an average annual increase in yields equal to 80 percent of the 1948-66 average would provide a national output of 126 million hundred pounds. This assumes that the total allotment of 2.2 million acres would be planted. Selected areas would not have sufficient water available to sustain this increase, and therefore production likely would fall short of the 126 million hundred pounds.

A 20 percent increase in the allotment to 2.4 million acres with

[1]Projection made by Grant and Shafer; See Chapter 3.

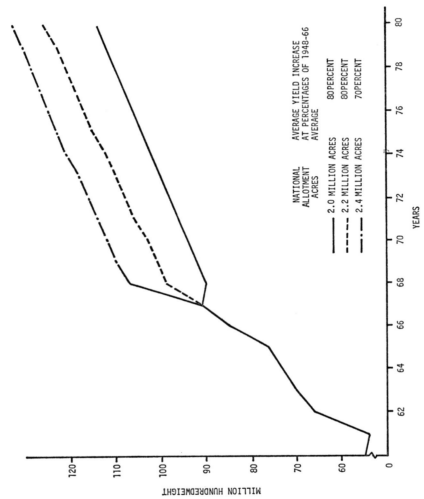

Figure 4-1. Projections of U. S. Rice Production to 1980 with Alternative Acreage Allotments and with Average Yield Increase at Selected Percentages of 1948-66 Average.

84

an average annual increase in yields equal to 70 percent of the 1948-66 average would provide a national output of 133 million hundred pounds, should the total acreage be planted. However, availability of water in selected areas would become even more critical in this situation, and unless the unplanted acreage in these areas could be sold or transferred to producers with sufficient water available the acreage planted likely would be appreciably less than the total allotment announced.

Information available on which to base projections indicates that a national output of 125 to 130 million hundred pounds would fully tax the resource base on a high proportion of the farms that presently have rice allotments, even with fairly optimistic projections of future yield increases attributable to technology. If it is reasonably certain that the total output needed by 1980 would exceed the 125 to 130 million hundred pound range, appropriate measures for increasing the production base would appear to be in order. This could be accomplished by the suspension of marketing quotas, which would likely occur because a requirement of this magnitude would mean that total supply would be less than normal supply. Should suspension of marketing quotas fail to produce the quantity of rice required, then suspension of acreage allotments may also be necessary.

Rice Production Potential in the United States

Should the need for rice exceed 125-130 million hundredweight, which is near the limits of the resource base of farmers with rice allotments, the question of potential production capability in the United States becomes relevant for consideration. For the southern rice producing states, this question was recently researched in considerable detail.[2] Within this area there are some 8.5 million acres of cropland suitable for rice production. Available water for irrigation along with agronomic limitations associated with rotation programs would permit sustained annual plantings in the southern region of about 3.6 million acres of rice. However, prices received for rice in relation to prices received for competing enterprises would be the ultimate determinant of the level of rice production.

Assuming no constraints on either the production of rice or of those enterprises which may compete for the land resources on which rice could be grown, the aforementioned study estimates that farmers in the southern region would plant between 2.8 and 3.3 million acres of rice if the price expectations were $4 per hundredweight. This estimate reckons with prices and returns which farmers in the region

---

[2]"Resource Use Adjustments in Southern Rice Areas, Part I, Effects of Price Changes with Unrestricted Rice Acreages"; Southern Cooperative Series Bulletin 122, June 1967.

might obtain from enterprises that are competitive with rice. Translated into production potentials the analysis suggests that producers in the southern region could grow between 140 and 160 million hundredweight of rice on a sustained basis in the absence of production constraints and taking into account the rotation requirements and anticipated returns from competitive enterprises.

This potential production of rice in the southern region would entail some substantial changes in the relative importance of producing areas compared to the current situation. Major expansion in production would take place in the Mississippi Delta, Northeast Arkansas, Southwest Louisiana and the Central area of Texas. Owing primarily to limited water resources, comparatively little production increase would be expected in the Grand Prairie of Arkansas and in the eastern area of Texas.

The foregoing estimate does not take into account the prospects for increased rice production in California and in the minor producing regions of the United States. However, evidence indicates that production potentials in other regions are comparable to those in the southern region. Hence, it would appear that there is substantial latent capability by U. S. farmers to meet future requirements well in excess of existing levels of rice production, and well beyond the 125-130 million hundredweight production capability that would appear to constitute the upper limits of output on farms that now have rice allotments.

An Examination of Policy Alternatives

In this section, the authors' statements are extended beyond those of a positive analysis of the economics of the rice industry. Normative statements relating to public policy goals that appear feasible for certain groups in society are made. Such statements are generally considered "off-limits" for economists, hence a brief justification appears to be in order. It is assumed that within the foreseeable future, society will continue to implement public programs through the instrument of government and that their programs will be directed toward fostering an orderly functioning rice industry and supporting the economic welfare of rice producers. The past and present government programs for rice provide ample evidence that this assumption probably is most valid. Within this context, the attempt is to examine the needs of the various groups that are primarily influenced by government rice policy and to enunciate what appear to be reasonable policy objectives for each of these groups. These objectives then provide a framework for the subsequent evaluation of alternative farm programs for rice.

A Consideration of Basic Policy Objectives

From the viewpoint of the public at large a requirement of any measures taken by state or federal agencies for the primary concern of one segment of society is that in the long run it serves to the total benefit of all, and that the distribution of such benefits is fair and equitable between groups. This general principle underlies and provides the basis for numerous public actions, policy measures and legislation instruments which make up the regulatory framework under which our democracy operates. This is the public interest side of all measures promoted by any given group, and in evaluating specific programs and program alternatives the question of net social benefit and equitable treatment must be kept in mind. It is through the public interest aspect that we justify expenditures to special groups, such as direct payments to farmers, at times when effective demand fails to produce prices that will provide fair and equitable returns through the marketplace. Preserving the production integrity of the rice industry is no doubt a question of public interest.

At the same time the public interest is equally involved in reverse situations. When consumer demands and export requirements expand rapidly and exceed former levels of output, the public interest is served by measures that will foster orderly expansion. This might involve several actions, such as (1) special financial assistance to farmers and industry groups if additional capital is needed to increase output, and (2) special provisions to permit resources in the hands of new producers to come into use if it is determined that in the long run an expanded production base is needed.

In considering alternative approaches that would optimize the total contributions of the rice industry to society as a whole, perspective in regard to the public interest must be maintained. It is important to recognize this necessity when examining the needs of various segments of the industry and of society.

The effects of a rice program are of primary importance to four major interest groups in the United States: (1) rice producers, (2) rice consumers, (3) the complex of firms involved in storage, processing, distribution and primary utilization of rice and (4) the Federal government, the vehicle by which programs designed to benefit all concerned are administered. From each of these perspectives, a particular policy and program may have unique features and widely different potential consequences. The adequacy of a program may, and often will, depend upon the vantage point from which it is viewed. Most important of all, there may be conflicts of interest among the groups—particularly the first three. No policy or program is likely to resolve all such conflicts, but an enunciation of reasonable policy objectives from the standpoint of each sector provides a useful framework for examining alternative approaches to the problem and for insuring that those sectors of the economy that will be most affected receive the attention and consideration they deserve.

TABLE 4-3. U.S. EXPORTS OF MILLED RICE UNDER SPECIFIED GOVERNMENT-FINANCED PROGRAMS, JULY-JUNE 1954-66

| Fiscal year | Public law 480 | | | | | P.L. 655 Section 402 Sales for foreign currency and economic aid | Total Exports under specified government programs |
	Title I Sales for foreign currency	Title II Famine and other emergency relief	Title III Foreign donation[1]	Title III Barter[2]	Title IV Long-term credit		
				1,000 cwt.			
1954-55		305		5		1	311
1955-56	2,530	1,943	865	197		563	6,089
1956-57	18,127	549	2,175	657		248	21,756
1957-58	5,094	483	596	8		153	6,334
1958-59	3,767	40	541	2,552			6,900
1959-60	9,960	575	1,417	683		162	12,797
1960-61	11,906	404	1,751	348		93	14,502
1961-62	8,612	440				494	9,546
1962-63	12,742	14			770	341	13,867
1963-64	13,211				1,072	593	14,876
1964-65	11,004				759	38	11,801
1965-66	6,917				716	2,008	9,641

[1] Foreign donations are authorized under Section 416 of the Agricultural Act of 1949 and Section 302, Title III, P.L. 480.
[2] The barter program is authorized under the Charter Act of the Commodity Cedit Corp.; Section 303, Title III, P.L. 480; and other legislation.
Source: USDA, *Rice: Annual Market Summary*, 1961-1966 issues.

Producer Perspective

A broad policy objective for rice producers is to find means whereby efficient farm operators may earn returns on resources devoted to rice production comparable to the returns to similar resources employed in other segments of the agricultural and general economy. The problem of U. S. rice producers in the past has been analogous to that of other producer segments of agriculture—a problem of resource adjustment.

Increasing production efficiency, accomplished by larger capital investments in resource inputs, and advancing technology result in increased production. Increased production, coupled with the inelastic nature of demand for farm products, creates an unfavorable imbalance between supply and demand. While improving their productive methods in an attempt to reduce costs, producers often find themselves in the paradoxical position of receiving little or no reward for their efforts to achieve higher efficiency. This is manifested by relatively low farm prices, decreasing returns to productive resources and declining incomes for producers.[3] In short, although the costs of technological advancement are incurred by producers. the benefits involved are not retained in the producer sector. This problem is appropriately a matter of public concern and has been the wellspring of governmental policy for agriculture in the past.

In meeting its obligations to rice producers, a national rice program should have as one of its major objectives the promotion of continued technological advancements in production. Further, a program should provide for assistance in the adjustment problems created by these advancements so that producers may share in the social benefits accruing from their own efforts.

Rice is the major commodity consumed by populations of nations in many parts of the world, especially in the Far East. In recent years it has played an increasingly important role in U. S. international policy implementation through providing a partial means of meeting foreign aid commitments to such countries. The use of rice industry productive resources to meet the needs of the nation's international political goals is a somewhat unique feature of the industry which should receive special consideration from the producer perspective. The need or demand for "policy" is not reflected through commonly identified market forces. Instead, the requirement is in substantial measure determined, at least in past national economy. Clearly, any program which supports the income of producers will involve social

---

[3]All those magnitudes by which producers' welfare is measured must be considered in relation to the general economic environment. Hence, in a period of general inflation in the economy, as has been the experience of the last decade, "inadequate" levels of prices and incomes may result not so much from decreasing as from constant levels, or even from rates of increase that are slower than that of the remainder of the economy.

costs which ultimately must be borne by society as a whole. These costs may be borne by society through either higher market prices for rice or through U. S. Treasury payments supported by taxes, or some combination of the two.

The per capita consumption of rice is unequally distributed over the nation's income categories. Per capita consumption among low income families is significantly higher than among medium and higher income families (Table 4-4). Hence, the costs of supporting a rice program through higher market prices would be borne most heavily by the low income segment of the U. S. society. Placing the cost burden of a program on the low income segment of the population is in considerable measure contrary to the broad national policy of the United States which focuses on improving the economic and social conditions for this group. This apparent conflict with the broader national policy suggests the need for a wider dispersal of program costs. It would appear that funding from the U. S. Treasury would be desirable and more consistent with our overriding national goals than a program which attempts to effect income transfers to the farm sector from those low income groups who are the major consumers of rice.

Marketing Firm Complex Perspective

Adjustment problems created by U. S. rice programs also must be considered from the standpoint of the complex of firms involved

TABLE 4-4. CONSUMPTION OF RICE PER HOUSEHOLD, PERCENT OF HOUSEHOLDS USING RICE AND PERCENTAGE USE DISTRIBUTIONS, BY INCOME GROUPS IN THE U.S., ONE-WEEK, 1965

Annual income (dollars per year)	Pounds per household	Percent of households using	Percentage use distribution[1]	Cumulative percentage use distribution
All households	.44	31.4	100.0	
Under 1,000	.59	39.5	6.7	6.7
1,000 - 1,999	.57	32.8	11.6	18.3
2,000 - 2,999	.64	33.9	13.1	31.4
3,000 - 3,999	.70	34.8	16.3	47.7
4,000 - 4,999	.47	30.7	10.8	58.5
5,000 - 5,999	.45	30.8	13.9	72.4
6,000 - 6,999	.44	31.2	10.0	82.4
7,000 - 7,999	.26	38.0	4.8	87.2
8,000 - 8,999	.29	31.0	3.9	91.1
9,000 - 9,999	.22	28.7	2.1	93.2
10,000 -14,999	.28	31.4	5.0	98.2
15,000 - Over	.30	25.6	1.8	100.0

[1]Household use by income class was developed from the product of pounds per household times the number of households in each class.

Source: *Food Consumption of Households in the United States, Spring, 1965,* Household Food Consumption Survey, 1965-1966, Report No. 1, Agricultural Research Service, USDA, Spring, 1965.

in the drying, storing, milling, distributing and processing of this crop. In the past, little attention has been given to the adjustment problems of this complex of firms that may arise from program changes or technological advancements in the industry. If these firms have more control over their investments than producers, their adjustment problems may be generally less severe than those which confront producers. On the other hand, the comparatively small number of firms involved may mean that their adjustment problems are simply overshadowed by those involving vastly larger numbers of producer firms.

Regardless of which of the foregoing is the most accurate depiction of the position of the marketing firm complex, it is apparent that these firms constitute a vital part of the rice industry. For it is this complex of firms on which society must depend for efficiency in the marketing process, and for this reason it is important that their interests be given consideration in evaluating program alternatives.

It may be expected that the operations of rice marketing and processing firms will be affected by both changes in the volume of rice marketed and changes in price that may result from a specific program. The cost of handling rice from the initial points of storage, through mills, wholesalers and retailers is influenced by the volume handled. Such firms constitute the readily identifiable market complex involved in the handling and distribution of rice.

But in addition, there are firms of relevance which use rice as inputs in their manufacturing processes. The decision to use rice or some competing grain by such firms is materially influenced by the input costs of rice relative to those of substitutable products. The interchangeability of rice and other grains in beer manufacture is a prime example of such substitution. The firms using rice as a manufacturing input are typically large scale. Consequently, the decision to shift from rice to a competing grain may have a substantial impact on the national demand for rice and on commercial market price.

Hence, policy considerations from the perspective of the marketing firm complex must reckon both with the impact of alternative programs in two dimensions. First, there are the potential effects on the efficiency with which the marketing task is accomplished. Second, there are the potential effects on the demands of those firms which use rice as inputs in manufacturing or conversion operations.

Government Perspective

The objectives or the obligation of government cannot be clearly distinguished from those discussed previously. As the representative of society, the government's objective should be the minimization of program costs while fulfilling policy objectives. The minimization objective should be considered in the broad context of social costs, and it is important to recognize that there are several components or possible manifestations of such costs. First, there are the treasury costs of program operations. Second, there are costs of both an absolute or opportunity nature associated with program effects on the efficiency with which rice is produced and distributed. Finally, there are costs which are manifested in prices which consumers must pay for rice. All of these aspects of costs should be taken into account when considering the means by which government action can minimize the cost of a program to society.

The cost minimization objectives of the federal establishment is further confounded by the fact that a policy and implementing program must reckon with a problem which has two dimensions. In addition to accommodating the domestic U. S. requirements for rice, approaches taken by the government must provide for the production of substantial quantities of this commodity to meet international commitments or needs. The involvement and importance of rice as a commodity which is used as an instrument of international politics poses special problems that are not directly considered in the preceding discussion of policy objectives. However, it is important that this international dimension be kept in mind when evaluating the relative merits of policy alternatives for the rice industry.

The Present Program:
Acreage Allotments and Marketing Quotas

In essence, the program now employed for the rice industry entails restricting the amount of land that can be used for rice production in order to obtain a target level of output. A support price guarantee provides the incentive for rice producers to conform to the production objectives established by the government. Production in excess of the amount that can be sold commercially at or above the support level moves into the hands of the government. Since U. S. support prices for rice generally have been above those prevailing in world markets, export subsidies also have been an integral part of the program. The details of the program under which the rice industry now operates have been presented earlier. The purpose here is to examine the current program from the perspectives of those groups that are affected by its operation.

The program focuses directly on insuring producers a price that the public regards as equitable for their activities. Producers who abide by the production restraints established by the government are virtually insured of a predetermined price which abstracts from market supply and demand conditions. Hence, there is little question regarding the capabilities of the program to provide the desired level of producer support. Further, the acreage restriction provisions of the program have latent possibilities of constraining production to the end of accomplishing a convergence of support and commercial market prices for rice. The demand for rice is inelastic, hence, relatively small changes in supply have rather substantial effects on price. Estimates indicate that a 1 percent change in rice supplies will produce a price change of approximately 3.7 percent in the opposite direction. Thus, a 1 percent reduction in supplies can be expected to bring about an upward price adjustment of about 3.7 percent.[4] However, there have been few occasions under the existing program when the comparatively high responsiveness of price to a short supply situation has been of advantage to producers. Production technology gains have increased yields with such rapidity that output has increased despite acreage allotments. The converse price depressing effects of a condition of oversupply historically has been the major problem of concern.

Viewed from the long run perspective of the producer, however, one major limitation of the program becomes apparent. The acreage allotment and attendant price supports constitute a franchise that is an advantage largely accruing to those producers who initially receive them. The value of this franchise tends to be capitalized, and is largely dissipated with the first transfer of farm ownership.

In examining the present program, it is important to recognize that the major preoccupation of the past has been on supply restricting measures. This may be in sharp contrast to the future situation where the United States may be called upon to substantially increase rice output to meet world needs.[5] Holders of existing rice allotments may be hard pressed to produce the amount of rice required in the future with the resource base they now have. Moreover, should they be able to do so, it would appear that the intensification required would tend to escalate unit production costs.

Through using price supports as the mainstay of its approach, the existing program transfers a substantial share of total program costs to rice consumers. It was pointed out earlier that the heavy consumers of rice in the United States are the low income groups. Thus, the existing program in some measure runs counter to other national policies designed to enhance the living standards of the lower income segments of U. S. society.

From the standpoint of certain firms in the marketing complex, internal adjustment problems were rather severe during the initial stages of the existing program. The reduction in the volume of

---

[4]Grant, Warren R., "A Model for Estimating Costs of Government Export Progams for Rice," *Agricultural Economics Research*, ERS, U.S.D.A., Volume 19, No. 3, July 1967. Grant estimated the price elasticity of demand at $-.27$. The values used above were obtained by transforming this estimate into a price flexibility estimate. In doing so no allowance was made for substitution between rice and other products as the price of rice increased. Hence, the above estimate may be regarded as the minimum response of price to a change in rice supplies.

[5]See Shafer and Grant, Chapter 2.

rice produced and marketed caused excess capacity and attrition problems among firms engaged in drying, storage and milling. However, during the intervening years, this adjustment problem has been largely obviated by the attrition process and as a result of increased per-acre yields that have pushed production steadily upward. There is little evidence to suggest that continued operation under the existing program would create future adjustment problems for these firms. For firms that use rice as a manufacturing input, however, the comparatively high product cost inherent in the system of price supports has a disadvantage. The level of support restricts in some measure the extent to which such firms use rice in their operations.[6]

Viewed from the perspective of the government and of society, the costs of the present program for the rice industry fall into two categories: (1) the costs borne by rice consumers in the form of retail prices consistent with the support level at which the price of rice is maintained and (2) treasury costs involved in maintaining the desired support price level. About one-third of the total U. S. rice production is consumed domestically, and consumers bear approximately this proportionate share of the total program costs. Taxpayers in general bear about two-thirds of program costs in the form of treasury expenditures for export subsidies, acquisition and storage costs, free domestic distribution and for foreign aid and assistance. The relative shares of the burden borne by rice consumers and the broader base of taxpayers through treasury costs will vary considerably depending upon supply conditions. Under conditions of short supply when little involvement of the government may be required to support the desired price level for rice, the burden would fall largely on consumers and on government assistance programs.[7] Conversely, under

---

[6] Effect of price upon the level of industrial utilization of rice have been voiced on many occasions. For recent examples see: *Food and Agriculture Act of 1965: Hearings Before the Committee on Agriculture for the United States Senate*, 89th Congress, 1st Session, Statements of Mr. William K. Coors, Mr. Richard J. Bender, and Mr. James Rowe.

[7] As long as the domestic program contains measures that restrict production response, the existence of market prices above the U. S. support level (such as is the case at this writing) does not negate the fact that there are consumer costs as well as Treasury costs for the program. As Shafer and Grant point out in Chapter 3, the United States accounted for almost one-fifth of the world exports of rice in 1966, and 58 percent of the U. S. rice supply was exported during the 1966-67 marketing year. Clearly, the restrictive aspect of the U. S. program, resulting from acreage allotments, is a major determinant of world rice prices as well as of domestic prices. Therefore, it is logical to expect that equilibrium rice prices, established on the basis of freedom of producer entry and freedom of producer expansion, likely would be lower than those currently in existence. Hence, there are presently social costs of the program even though no export subsidy payments or CCC acquisitions are being made. These costs result from the fact that consumers must pay higher prices for rice, and treasury costs of government for rice purchases to meet commitments to foreign and domestic aid programs are higher than would be the case in the absence of marketing quotas and acreage allotments.

conditions of excessive supply which would entail substantial involvement of the government to support the desired price level, the preponderance of the burden would fall on the Treasury and consequently on taxpayers in general.

Marketing Quotas Without Acreage Allotments

The substitution of quantity production controls for the marketing quotas based on acreage allotments currently in existence has been proposed as an alternative to the present program. This would consist of hundredweight quotas for rice. It is assumed that these quotas would be allocated to states, counties and farms in approximately the same manner as are the present marketing quotas using historical acreage as a base. The main difference would be that producers would be allocated a maximum sales quota rather than an acreage allotment.

Changing the output restraint from a restriction on acreage planted to one of hundredweights marketed could have a significant impact on the efficiency with which rice is produced. Fixing the quantity that can be produced rather than the acreage on which rice can be grown would afford considerable latitude for producers to engage in per unit cost minimization practices for their entire farming enterprise. Emphasis would be shifted from practices which serve to increase per acre yields to those of fulfilling marketing quotas with the least possible cost combination of resources. This would likely mean that part of the off-farm resources presently devoted to rice production could be transferred into the production of alternative crops, and that additional land could be employed in the production of rice. If these changes result in greater efficiency of rice production, it may be possible to support producers' net incomes at essentially the same level as at present with lower support prices.

In Arkansas, Mississippi and Southwest Louisiana which now have farm-based acreage allotments, the separation of marketing quotas from the land resource would have still another effect at the producer level. Since the franchise to produce would be associated with the producer and not with the land, the capitalization of this production right could be shifted from the land resource, and substantial reductions in the value of present rice acreage could result. Further, the separation of the right to produce from land would increase the freedom of rice producers to shift non-land productive resources between regions. Hence, some regional relocation of rice production may result. The extent to which these shifts occur would depend both upon the rice production efficiency differentials and differences in the profitability of alternatives among regions.

Evidence suggests, however, that negotiability of the right to produce rice may take place with less rapidity and to a less extent than these theoretical considerations would suggest. Rice acreage allotments are producer based rather than farm based in Texas, California and the delta portion of Louisiana. These producer-based allotments are negotiable. A recent study of allotment transfers made in Texas reveals only limited production shifts from the less productive to the more productive counties of the state as a result of negotiability.[8]

The proportion of the social costs of the program borne by consumers would not differ materially from that of the existing program. Consumers would continue to bear a substantial portion of the total program costs since the income transfer to rice producers from consumers would continue to be supported through market prices. Costs incurred for export subsidy payments and government domestic and international aid programs would not differ materially from those of the present program.

If divorcing marketing quotas from the land resource results in regional production relocation, as mentioned above, concomitant regional adjustments in drying, storing and milling facilities would be required. This could result in excess capacity in these facilities in some present rice producing areas. Other than these relocation problems, it would appear that few additional adjustments would be required by the marketing firm complex segment of the industry. The price and quantity dimensions of a marketing quota program differ little from those of the existing program.

Multiple Price Plans for Rice

The two-price plans which have been proposed for rice differ considerably in the method of operation and extent of government control.[9] They all have a similar objective, the transfer of income from domestic consumers to the producers. The plans are based on the principle of discriminatory marketing between separate markets of different demand characteristics.

Necessary conditions for the success of a two-price plan are that (a) the total market can be separated into two parts—in the case of rice, the domestic market and the export market; (b) tariffs and/or quotas insulate the high price domestic market from imports of the

---

[8]Welsh, Delane E., "Effect of Producer-Based, Negotiable Rice Acreage Allotments on Location of Rice Production in Texas," (Unpublished Manuscript), Department of Agricultural Economics and Sociology, Texas A&M University, College Station, Texas.

[9]"A Study of Various Two-Price Systems of Price Support and Marketing Which Could Be Made Applicable to Rice," 84th Congress, 1st Session, House Document No. 100, United States Government Printing Office, Washington, D. C., 1955, and George L. Mehren, *Multiple Price Plans for Rice,* California Agricultural Experiment Station, Mimeographed Report No. 175, April 1955.

low-price export market; and (c) the demand in the domestic market is price inelastic relative to the demand in the export market.

Grant found that the price elasticity of demand for rice in the domestic market was −0.27; that is, a 1.0 percent change in the domestic price affects domestic consumption 0.27 percent in the opposite direction.[10] Grant also estimated that the price elasticity of demand in the export market was about six times that in the domestic market. A 1.0 percent change in the export price was inversely related to a 1.54 percent change in quantity exported.

Farm income to rice producers under a two-price plan is maintained through relatively high-level price protection in the domestic market while exporting the excess of domestic production at world prices.

Under most versions of the multiple price plan, controls and restrictions on production are replaced with the use of product bases. Farmers receive higher prices for base production than for excess or overbase production. In the case of rice, the domestic-foreign market division may mean that rice producers would be allowed to expand production, but would receive price supports only on that part of their total production sold in the domestic market. Each producers' foreign sales would be made at world prices which depend upon the existing supply and demand for the quality, variety and type of rice that he markets.

Several procedures may be used to obtain for producers different prices for base production than for excess or overbase production. The technique most commonly adopted for agricultural commodities has been to impose a tax on domestic buyers of the commodity and to return the proceeds from this tax to producers on their base production. This procedure could be implemented for the rice industry through the use of negotiable marketing certificates, issued to each producer in a quantity proportional to his historical or "normal" share of the domestic rice sales. Domestic processors, in turn, would be required to purchase these certificates in order to obtain rice for domestic uses. Thus, two prices for rice would be received by farmers —market or world prices for that part of production moving into the foreign market, and market price plus the value of certificates for rice being sold in the domestic market.

Producers' incomes under a two-price program would depend on the value of domestic marketing certificates, the quantity sold in the domestic market and the world price of rice. The entire support of producers' incomes, above free market levels, must come from within the domestic market. Considering the relatively small percentage of United States rice sold in the domestic market, it is questionable

[10]Grant, *Agricultural Economics Research*, 19 (3), July 1967.

that domestic prices could be raised sufficiently to return to producers a level of gross income deemed equitable or as high as that from alternative programs. The restraint on increasing domestic prices stems not from economic feasibility but from the practical matter of public resistance to the increase that would be required.

Adoption of a multiple price plan for rice would precipitate a rather significant localization of the cost burden of supporting producers' incomes within society. The substantial upward adjustment in domestic retail prices would place the burden of cost mainly on low income families and certain ethnic groups—the major consumers of table rice. Government treasury costs would fall well below that of the existing program, and in the absence of export subsidy payments, the only cost incurred by the Treasury would be the cost of administering the two-price plan.

This argument is supported by estimates made for 1966 using the domestic and world demand equations developed by Grant.[11] A comparison is made of changes in the distribution of social costs that would have accrued if the present acreage allotment-marketing quota program had been replaced with a two-price program. For the two-price program, these estimates assume that a set of world and domestic prices existed in 1966 that make the gross income to U. S. rice producers equivalent to that estimated for the 1966 one-price program. Total production was assumed to be the same under both programs. As shown in Table 4-5 the use of a two-price plan for rice would have caused a shift of 2.6 million hundredweight from

[11]*Ibid.*

TABLE 4-5. COMPARISONS OF ESTIMATED DOMESTIC UTILIZATION, EXPORTS AND COSTS OF ALTERNATIVE PRICE PROGRAMS WITH 1966 DATA[1]

Item	Unit	Two-price program Estimated[2]	1966 one-price program Estimated[3]
Domestic utilization	Million cwt.	31.5	34.1
Exports	Million cwt.	53.3	50.7
Total subsidy	Million dollars	0	36.5
Additional cost to domestic consumers	Million dollars	35.0	0

[1]Two stage lease squares equations with 1963 data used in deriving estimates. See: Grant, *Agricultural Economics Research*, 19 (3), July 1967.

[2]Domestic price at $10.49 milled basis or $5.42 rough, farm level basis and export price at the estimated 1966 world level ($7.58 milled basis).

[3]Estimate of price support program in effect in 1966, support price at $8.66 milled basis or $4.21 rough, farm level basis.

the domestic to the export market. Treasury costs for export subsidies would have been reduced by about $36.5 million. However, consumers would have had to bear an additional cost of about $35.0 million as a result of the price increase in the domestic market, Table 4-5. The estimated net savings under the two-price program was $1.5 million.[12]

Some Treasury outlays necessarily would be continued, consisting primarily of purchase and storage costs for rice needs of government for domestic and international aid programs filled through acquisitions in the open market. These costs historically have been allocated to the cost of the rice support program.

A program that further increases the domestic price for rice could cause significant adjustment problems for the domestic marketing system. The support of producers' incomes through higher domestic prices would place rice in an unfavorable price position relative to cereal grains that compete with and may be substituted for rice as an input in manufacturing. Higher domestic prices would increase present pressures to use these substitute grains in the place of rice. To the extent that the removal of production controls under this policy approach expands total supply, initial pressures for an expansion in facilities likely would be exerted on that part of the marketing system involved in drying, storing and milling. In the longer run, however, some economies of scale may be experienced by these firms that would not be realized under a program involving restrictions on production.

Compensatory Payments

Under this policy approach growers would market their rice at prices reflecting the consensus of the market based on the magnitude of supplies and the level of demand during the course of a harvesting and marketing season. Should this market consensus produce a price below the level regarded as the minimum necessary to produce equitable returns to rice farmers, then the difference between the price actually received and the price that the government determined producers should receive would be made up through direct payment to producers. Of necessity, market prices used to establish the basis for producer compensation from the government would be derived from a broad base of commercial market transactions. That is, market prices would be those established by national or regional marketing operations rather than those that might be obtained by individual producers or in highly local areas.

---

[12]It was necessary to resort to a statistical model as the means of comparing the two programs since only the one-price program was actually in effect. Statistical errors inherent in the demand equations employed in the model caused some discrepancy between the 1966 estimated and actual utilization of rice under the existing program. Actual utilization in the domestic market during 1966 was 32.6 million hundredweight, and actual exports were 52.0 hundredweight.

Although a system of compensatory payments could be instituted for the rice industry in the absence of either acreage allotments or marketing quotas, such is not likely to be the case. In the absence of constraints on either production or marketing, the cost to the government of supporting prices or rice producer incomes at or near existing levels would be prohibitied because of the high output response that would likely occur if acreage constraints were removed. Consequently, a compensatory payment approach would entail limitation on the ability of producers to either grow or market rice as an integral part of the program.

From the standpoint of producers, the compensatory payment approach provides analogous treatment to a program based on price supports with acreage controls and surplus stock accumulation. The nature of the price or income guarantee to the producer would be essentially the same under either arrangement. The major difference would be in the form by which the income transfer is made to the producer sector from the remainder of the economy. In the case of compensatory payments, the income transfer is accomplished through direct payments equal to the disparity betwen the price farmers actually received for their rice crop and the price that national policy decreed to be equitable. Under the price support approach an equitable market price is determined and maintained by buying and storage operations on the part of the government. Both methods entail treasury outlays that must be supported by taxes.

From the standpoint of rice consumers, the direct payment approach would clearly constitute an equitable situation. The prices that consumers would pay for rice would be a function of the supply available and the quantity demanded. Since short-term market equilibrium would characterize marketing conditions for the crop, carryover in supplies would reflect the industry judgment regarding anticipated requirements. The result may be some variability in supplies and prices that consumers would not experience under a price support and stabilization scheme involving the extensive control and management of rice stocks by the government. Moreover, the fact that the government itself may become a major component of the market demand in order to meet unanticipated requirements for rice to be used as an instrument in international politics may serve to further contribute to the short-term instability in consumer rice prices.

The marketing firm complex would also appear to have sufficient latitude for adjustment in operations under a compensatory payment approach. Flow of product into the market would vary only to the extent normally anticipated due to seasonality in production, vagaries of the weather, and perhaps, varying requirements of the government. While precipitous changes in the level of support could bring about the need for correspondingly sharp adjustments in the operations of marketing firms, it appears that such changes are neither more likely to occur nor more fraught with difficulties than changes under other policy approaches that may have volume implications to rice marketing firms. Firms using rice or rice products as inputs for manufacturing operations would be insured of continuing supplies at competitive prices at all times since the market price of rice would be established by the full spectrum of demand forces. This would include the prices of products that constitute potential substitutes for rice in the operations of such firms.

Social costs of a program based on compensatory payments to farmers would appear to be about the same as that for a program based on price supports and surplus acquisition and control by the government. Given equal price or income objectives for each type of program, the net income transfer from the remainder of society to rice farmers would not differ materially. However, the burden of the income transfer would be less for the low income segments of the economy under the compensatory payment approach than for one involving price supports and management of surplus inventories. Under either approach the progressive nature of the U. S. tax structure tends to place the burden of treasury cost on the middle and high income segments of the population. But heavy rice consumption takes place largely within the low income groups of the country. The compensatory payment method of supporting farm prices would insure this group a plentiful supply of rice at a price established by the market forces reflecting conditions of supply and the level of demand for rice. This price level would, of course, vary depending upon the restrictive measures that the government employed in controlling the total production of rice, but it would in all cases be below the price that consumers would have to pay for an equivalent quantity of production under a system of comparable acreage controls and an artificially established support price.

Conservation Reserve

A conservation reserve program is considered herein as a possible approach to bring about an equitable balance between rice supply and total rice demand. In large part, the continuing problem of imbalance in this regard has resulted from rapid increases in the productive efficiency of resources used in rice production, resulting from improved technology and increased uses of capital. The removal of acreage committed to rice production is a possible approach to restricting supply to market demand, thereby holding resources idle in an attempt to avoid the production of surpluses.

Several types of land retirement or conservation reserve programs have been recommended for use for various commodities in the past. These may involve annual or long-term lease, partial or whole farm retirement, or some combination of these. The objectives of these various approaches are largely the same, however, and their effects on various sectors of the rice industry generally are highly similar.

The conservation reserve approach offers producers an opportunity for improved incomes with few associated restrictions on their farming operations. If sufficient acreage is shifted out of rice production to effectively restrict supply to market demand, farm prices and producers' incomes can be maintained at desired levels. It should be recognized, however, that land removal will not necessarily result in supply restriction. Increased applications of other productive resources, primarily capital, could increase yields sufficiently to allow the same or increased production on less acreage. In fact, this has been the experience of many acreage restriction programs in the past.[13] Further, if the annual rate of increase in productive efficiency continues to be more rapid than the rate of expansion in demand in the future, continued removal of rice acreage would be required each year.

A conservation reserve program could offer efficiency advantages over current acreage restriction and allotment approaches. Past experience with conservation reserve programs for other commodities indicates that the most active participants in such a program are producers operating least efficient acreage, including older farmers near retirement age.[14] Furthermore, substantial relocation of production into the more efficient producing regions would be anticipated. Consequently, production could be shifted into the hands of more efficient enterprises and overall costs of production would be lowered.

The social costs of a conservation reserve program would be distributed between consumers, who would pay in the form of market prices, and taxpayers who would pay in the form of higher treasury costs. Most of these social costs, however, would be borne by taxpayers. Treasury funds would be required for conservation or diversion payments to producers who participate in the program and divert all or part of their acreage from rice production. These treasury costs would be partially offset, however, by a reduction in the costs of current government price support, and storage operations.

Increases in consumer prices would be expected to result from the restriction of rice supplies. Consumers of milled rice would be affected most by higher retail prices. Consumers of rice products, which involve substantial processing as well as other commodities, would be affected to a lesser extent. Although the conservation reserve program would maintain farm prices at levels above those

---

[13]J. Carroll Bottum, "Voluntary Land Retirement," *The Farm Problem—What Are the Choices?*, Agricultural Extension Service, The Ohio State University, Columbus, Ohio.
[14]*Ibid.*

which would prevail if there were no incentive payments inducing farmers to take land out of rice production, prices for rice would probably be below those existing under price support and storage programs.

From the standpoint of the marketing firm complex, internal industry adjustment problems would be anticipated. As rice production was allowed to move to more efficient producing regions, in the absence of acreage allotments, corresponding regional shifts in drying, storage and milling operations would be expected. The reductions in the volume of rice marketings would cause more adjustment problems for these firms than they have experienced under price support programs. If sufficient acreage is removed from rice production, excess capacity, especially in drying and storage facilities, would be expected to result. Similarly, other sectors of the rice industry such as farm service and supply firms and rural communities in the rice producing areas may be adversely affected by the reduction in rice production.

To the extent that domestic rice prices are increased by supply restriction above the level of world prices, export subsidy and import restriction schemes probably would need to remain in effect. At present, no export subsidy is paid for rice moving into foreign markets primarily because of an atypical foreign demand resulting from changes growing out of the Vietnam conflict. Moreover, the projections of future rice production and rice needs made by Shafer and Grant[15] indicate a growing deficit between rice importing and rice exporting countries within the foreseeable future. If this expanding need for rice in the world market is manifested by effective demand and consequently is reflected through commercial rice trade channels, little need will exist for export subsidy or import restriction schemes in the U. S. in the future. However, if this need must be fulfilled through government financed aid programs not directly related to effective demand in the world market, export subsidies and import restrictions would need to be given consideration.

Free Market

The possibility of returning the rice industry to a marketing system free from government imposed production restrictions and price or income supports continues to receive much attention. Indeed, recent expansions in the demand for rice, particularly in the foreign market, have created a quite favorable price position for U. S.-produced rice with season average prices received by farmers remaining above support levels. This has led some to believe that the time is right for the withdrawal of government activity in the rice industry.

---

[15]See Shafer and Grant: Chapter 2.

As used herein, a free market for rice means the removal of acreage allotments and other production restrictions and the abandonment of price and income support programs for rice producers. Export subsidy payments by government to domestic exporters of rice would also be discontinued. It is assumed, however, that such government programs as are needed to satisfy foreign and domestic aid commitments would remain in effect, that is, P.L. 480, domestic donations and other food aid programs would be continued.

The return to a free market for rice would cause significant adjustment problems and considerable economic stress for some rice producers. The immediate effect of releasing rice-producing acreage previously restricted by allotments probably would be substantially increased rice production. Prices at the farm level and producers' incomes would be expected to fall sharply as a result of this expanded production, coupled with the highly inelastic domestic demand for rice.[16] Estimates show that a release of rice allotments would result in a decline in domestic rice prices to levels consistent with world prices. It has been estimated that if such action had been taken in 1960, U. S. domestic farm level prices for rice in 1965 would have been $3.00 per hundredweight, or about two-thirds of the 1965 support price.[17]

In the longer run, resources most likely would be shifted out of rice production and into more profitable alternative enterprises eventually establishing a balance between production and market demand at prices determined by free market conditions. In addition to shifts away from rice production in the long run, significant relocation of production among regions would be anticipated, with production concentrating in those areas that are best suited for and most efficient in rice production, relative to alternative opportunities.

These adjustments should lead to more efficient production of rice. However, under a free market system without government compensation, they would also mean substantial economic losses to many producers engaged in rice production. Least efficient producers and those with limited capabilities for expanding their operations would be most severely affected. In addition to farm income being lower, it would probably be more unstable than it is under the present price support program.

Rice consumers would benefit from a return to a free market through lower retail prices for rice. It is doubtful, however, if retail

---

[16]Grant estimates the domestic price elasticity to be −.27. See Grant, *Agricultural Economics Research,* 19 (3), July 1967.

[17]*Farm Price and Income Projections 1960-65 Under Conditions Approximating Free Production and Marketing of Agricultural Commodities,* Senate Document No. 77, January 1960.

prices would decline sufficiently to reflect fully the fall in farm level prices, since marketing costs constitute a sizable proportion of retail prices for rice in many outlets. Moreover, some of the marketing costs for such items as storage and interest necessary to distribute the seasonal production of rice evenly throughout the year currently are borne partially by government. In a free market, these costs would be transferred to the private marketing system and eventually passed on to rice consumers in the form of retail prices.

Taxpayers would be relieved of most of the public costs of price support and acreage restriction programs in a free market, although treasury costs required for operating foreign and domestic aid programs would continue. The needs of government for these purposes could be fulfilled by purchases in the open market. Government acquisitions for aid programs would continue to serve as an indirect support to producers' incomes as they have in the past.

Adjustment problems of the complex of marketing firms that handle rice created by a return to a free market likely would be substantial. With the initial release of acreage allotments and the subsequent increase in rice production, an expansion in marketing facilities would be required, especially facilities for storage and drying. As the rice market adjusts to a long run position of equilibrium between free market supply and demand, excess capacity in these facilities may result. More excess capacity in marketing facilities would be expected to exist in a free market than under present programs. The free market likely would result in wider year-to-year variations in production, and rice handlers and processors would tend to expand facilities to accommodate output in years of highest production. This increase in excess capacity would result in an efficiency loss for the industry as a whole.

Further, substantial relocation of marketing facilities would be expected to result from the expansion and contraction of rice production among regions. A recent study by Grant suggests the extent to which such relocation may occur in the absence of any restraints on production.[18] Much of the latent production capacity in the U.S. is in areas where no rice is produced. The development of production and supporting facilities in new regions may contribute further to excess capacity in areas which now produce rice.

SUMMARY

Government price support and acreage control programs in recent years, as well as the present program, have had as their main objective the implementation of restrictions on rice production in an effort to bring about a balance between supply and demand at prices that

[18]Grant, *Agricultural Economics Research,* 19 (3), July 1967.

would return rice producers equitable incomes. Such restrictions have been effected through acreage allotments and marketing quotas.

Projections made for this study indicate that policy needs of the foreseeable future may be largely reversed. That is, projected world "deficits" for rice may mean that the burden of future governmental rice policy will be that of examining U. S. rice production potentials and implementing programs to promote production expansion. If only modest changes in output are required, then normal increase in yields combined with comparatively small changes in acreage allotments within the current policy framework likely would permit annual production to be adjusted reasonably close to requirements. However, the projected deficits are of such magnitude that, if an attempt is made to fill them largely through increased U. S. output, then more than a modest upward adjustment in production will be required.

In this case, a suspension of the acreage allotment and marketing quota features of the present program, or a completely different set of program alternatives may need to be considered. A consideration of several feasible alternatives have been presented in this section. Although these policy alternatives are presented and analyzed separately, it is clear that they are not mutually exclusive. Many combinations of specific programs, as well as totally different approaches, can be visualized. The specific program alternatives examined in this section constitute plausible approaches to meeting the anticipated future needs for U. S.-produced rice.

Given their potential to cope with the anticipated market needs, alternative public programs for rice are examined from the standpoint of the needs of various groups in the industry and of society. The effects of the rice program are of primary importance to four major interest groups in the United States: (1) rice producers, (2) rice consumers, (3) the rice marketing firm complex and (4) the Federal government, the vehicle of program administration. From each perspective, a particular policy or program may have unique features—some desirable and some undesirable. Conclusions about the adequacy of a particular program often will depend upon the vantage point from which it is viewed and conflicts of interest among groups may arise. Such conclusions were not the purpose of this section. Rather, the purpose was to enunciate reasonable policy objectives from the standpoint of each sector, and, within this framework, to examine alternative policy approaches to problems of the southern rice industry. It is hoped that selection of a particular approach to be employed will be facilitated by this examination, but it is clear that such decisions transcend both the capabilities and responsibilities of the writers.

5

The Changing Rice Milling Industry

Randall Stelly
Harlon Traylor
Reid M. Grigsby

Approximately 40 to 42 rice milling firms in the United States handle the annual rice crop but not all operate every year. The mills are located in the producing areas adjacent to the supply of rough rice. Table 5-1 shows the number of milling firms operating in 1967, the range in daily milling capacity and the percentage of rice cooperatively milled in each of the major rice-producing states. The importance of cooperatives in the structure of the rice milling industry varies widely among states. A relatively high percentage of rice is cooperatively milled in California and Arkansas as compared to Texas and Louisiana.

Only one new rice mill has been installed in Texas since World War II. This one was built in 1963-64 and is of course more modern in design, installations and equipment than the other mills. However, most mills in Louisiana and Texas have installed new milling equipment, improved both rough and clean rice handling facilities and made some renovation to the basic facilities during the past five or ten years. Such renovation, modernization or new equipment include bulk rice receiving, handling and storage facilities for both rough and clean rice, new conveyors, bulk outloading and the installation of improved Japanese-made pearlers and rubber hullers. Some mills have also installed automatic processing controls and electronic sorting equipment.

TABLE 5-1. NUMBER OF MILLING FIRMS IN OPERATION, RANGE IN DAILY CAPACITY AND PERCENT OF RICE MILLED BY COOPERATIVES IN ARKANSAS, CALIFORNIA, LOUISIANA AND TEXAS, 1966-67 SEASON

States	Number of milling firms in operation			Range in daily (24 hours) milling capacity	Percentage of crop milled by cooperatives
	Cooperative	Other	Total	Hundredweight	
Arkansas	2	7	9	400 to 40,000	60 to 65
California	2	4	6	3,600 to 50,000	80 to 85
Louisiana	1	18	19	400 to 12,000	6 to 8
Texas	1	6	7	3,000 to 36,000	20 to 25

On the contrary, the rice parboiling process is relatively new in the U. S. and started in Texas on a commercial basis only during World War II. Therefore, with only one exception all parboiling plants in Louisiana and Texas have been constructed and put into operation during the past 20 years.

The attrition rate in rice mills in Louisiana and Texas has been rather heavy during the past five years. This is indicated by the following:

Number of Rice Mills Operating

	1962	1965	1966	1967
Louisiana	32	27	22	19
Texas	14	13	11	7
Total	46	40	33	26

Only about half as many mills were operating in the two states this past season as were operating 5 years ago. Forty-six mills operated in the two states in 1962, while only 26 operated in 1967. This reduction in the number of mills results from (1) the "folding-up" of small, independent, family owned and operated huller mills due mainly to increased competition for rough rice supplies and clean rice markets and (2) the consolidation of milling facilities by large multi-mill firms by closing-up their smaller, relatively inefficient mills in outlying areas and concentrating operations in the larger centrally located, more efficient milling operations.

MILLING CAPACITY

Total milling capacity has not been greatly affected by the reduction in the number of mills operating. The smaller mills usually are the ones that ceased operating. The remaining mills have increased their average capacity as well as their total output during the past few years through the installation of improved milling equipment and rice handling facilities, such as Japanese hullers and pearlers and bulk handling, storage and conveying systems.

For example, the mills in Texas that furnished information on this matter, and that were in operation 5 years ago, increased their combined total output from 5.79 million barrels in 1961-62 to 9.35 million barrels in 1966-67. The average output per mill increased from 1.16 million to 1.87 million barrels per season—an increase of 60 percent. Louisiana mills reported similar increases. The mills that responded milled 39 percent more rice in 1966-67 than they milled 5 years ago. Mills presently operating in the two states have the capacity to mill twice as much rice as is produced.

Texas mills normally operate year-round with about half of them operating 24 hours a day and the remainder operating two shifts, or 16 hours a day. Likewise, half the mills reported operating 7 days per week and the others only 5 days.

The mills interviewed in Texas reported a combined milling capacity of 24,742 hundredweight per 8-hour shift. These mills processed 11,550,000 barrels of rough rice during the 1966-67 season, or 467 times their combined capacity per 8-hour shift (on the basis of 100 pounds of clean rice outturn per barrel of rough rice).

The typical mill in Louisiana normally operates only from August to early May. A longer milling season would no doubt result in reducing the fixed overhead cost on a per barrel basis. Louisiana mills usually operate 24 hours per day during the peak fall season but only if the clean rice is moving out every day. Lack of clean rice storage space is the limiting factor with several mills and forces most mills in Louisiana to move out the clean rice immediately after milling it.

Rice milling in Louisiana and Texas is highly competitive and only the most efficient mills have been able to compete effectively and exhibit growth in recent years. Within the next 10 or 12 years, it is likely that not more than 8 to 10 mills will be operating in Louisiana and probably 5 in Texas. Further, it is anticipated that the smallest operating mills will have a capacity in excess of one million barrels of rough rice per year.

INTEGRATION AND CONSOLIDATION BY MILLS

During recent years, there has been a tendency by Louisiana mills to integrate their services and functions backward toward the producer. They have done this by erecting their own rough rice drying and storage facilities and engaging extensively in green rice purchasing and drying and storage operations for their own accounts. There are three basic reasons why mills have found this to their advantage. First, they can do their own blending and thus have better control over quality; second, there are costs savings in rough rice hauling and handling operations; and third, they can hedge on future price increase.

There are several opportunities for increasing mill revenue through integration. These include reducing rough rice hauling and handling costs, decreasing rice drying costs, more exact quality control, more efficient blending by commingling and possible increased volume of output. However, these income producing alternatives do not fully reflect the entire income possibilities and the transition now in process —especially in Louisiana. There is an attractive speculative element in storing rice from date of harvest to time of milling in anticipation of a price increase. This has no doubt stimulated the move toward green rice purchasing by Southern rice mills. Many mills (especially in Louisiana) apparently depend more on profits obtained through their rough rice procurement (or purchases on a green basis) and on drying and storage operations than they do on net margins on their milling operations. It is probable that mills will continue to expand their rough rice drying and storage facilities in order to accommodate increasing volumes of green rice purchases in the future.

There also has been some horizontal integration in the rice milling industry during the past few years. This has taken place through mergers, acquisition and/or consolidation of several milling units under one management. This process accounts for part of the previously mentioned 50 percent reduction in the number of rice mills that has taken place in Texas and Louisiana within the past 5 or 6 years. This has been accomplished through consolidation of milling facilities by large, multi-mill firms and the folding-up of small, independently owned mills.

The milling industry in Texas and Louisiana is likely to become more concentrated in the future. The trend toward integration and increased consolidation will no doubt continue as mills strive for increased economics of scale and compete more strenuously for the clean rice market. Further, increased capacity and efficiency through improvements in plant and facilities can be achieved only by sizeable capital outlays. This requirement for increased capitalization in equipment and facilities, and the working capital needed to finance rough rice inventory will make it more difficult for small rice mill operators to compete effectively in the future.

PACKAGING AND DISTRIBUTION OF CLEAN RICE

Approximately 75 percent of the rice milled in Texas during 1966 was packed in 100-pound bags, about 12 percent in consumer-size cartons of 5 pounds or less, 4 percent was sold in bulk and the remaining 9 percent was packed in either 25 or 50-pound bags. Texas rice mills have expanded or integrated their operations forward toward the consumer to a larger extent than has occurred in Louisiana. However, much of the output in Texas is still marketed in wholesale-type packages or in bulk. In Texas only two of the seven mills do not package milled rice in consumer size packages under their own brand names which they advertise in the major rice markets. In contrast, only 5 of the 19 mills operating in Louisiana operate this way.

All mills in both states depend heavily on the export market with sales abroad ranging from 40 to 99 percent of total output of individual mills. Western Europe, the Middle East, South Africa, Saudi Arabia and Canada are the principal export markets. Domestic sales are concentrated in the large northern and eastern centers of population and in the southern and southeastern states. While a large proportion of the rough rice supplies moves into the mills by truck, most of the clean rice is shipped out by rail.

Only four mills in Texas and four in Louisiana reported selling rice in foreign countries under their own accounts. The others sell to large grain exporters because (1) they have not developed their own markets or sales outlets in foreign countries, and (2) only the large mills have the capacity and/or volume to bid on government purchases that may be in lots ranging from 10,000 to 50,000 tons.

COSTS OF OPERATING RICE MILLS

A 1959 study presents the best available data on the cost of milling rice in the South.[1] Analysis of data from 23 mills in that study indicated an average total cost of 98 cents per 100 pounds of rough rice, Table 5-2. This included costs for all types of services. For purposes of conversion to a milled rice equivalent the authors used a milling yield of 69 percent, or 104 pounds of clean rice out-turn per barrel of rough rice. In the 23 mills included in that study the cost ranged from 63 cents to $1.48. Salaries, wages and commissions averaged 37 percent of the total cost, with production labor accounting for 20 cents, or over half of this amount. Packaging materials represented 21 percent of the total while administrative and selling expenses, excluding salaries, amounted to 17 percent. Utilities, supplies, repairs and maintenance, depreciation, taxes, insurance and storage made up the remainder, or 25 percent, of the total cost.

Three-fourths of all differences in total unit costs were the results of the volume of rice milled and the percentage of rice packaged in consumer-size containers.

[1]N. M. Thuroczy and W. A. Schlegel, *Costs of Operating Southern Rice Mills,* USDA - AMS Report #330, June 1959.

TABLE 5-2. AVERAGE COST TO MILLS FOR PROCESSING AND DISTRIBUTING 100 POUNDS OF ROUGH RICE, 1956-57 MILLING SEASON[1]

Cost item	Cents	Percent of total cost
1. Salaries and wages to production workers	20.0	20.2
2. All other salaries and commissions	17.1	17.2
3. Packaging material and bags	20.2	20.6
4. Buying, selling, general and administrative expenses (excluding salaries and commissions)	16.4	16.6
5. Depreciation	8.4	8.6
6. Plant operating expenses, utilities, repairs, maintenance	7.7	8.1
7. Outside storage of rough and milled rice	4.4	4.5
8. Taxes and all insurance	4.1	4.2
Total	98.3	100.0

[1]The source of data in Tables 1-5 is USDA, AMS, Report No. 330, *Cost of Operating Southern Rice Mills,* June 1959.

TABLE 5-3. MILLING AND MARKETING COSTS PER 100 POUNDS OF
ROUGH RICE MILLED IN MILLS WITH NO CONSUMER-SIZE PACKAGING
OPERATIONS, 1956-57

Cost item	Cents	Percent of total costs
Taxes and insurance	4.9	6.7
Depreciation	4.7	6.5
Wages and salaries to production workers	18.2	24.9
All other salaries	14.4	19.7
Utilities, repairs, maintenance	6.4	8.8
Packaging material[1]	12.8	17.5
Selling, general and administrative	11.6	15.9
Total	73.0	100.0

[1]Burlap bags and twine.

Total costs for mills which did not package the rice averaged
73 cents per 100 pounds of rough rice and ranged from 63 to 94 cents,
depending largely upon the scale of milling operations, (Table 5-3).
Wages and salaries to production workers in these mills represented
about 25 percent of the total cost, and other salaries and commissions
represented about 20 percent. The cost of bags was about 18 percent,
while selling and administrative expenses (excluding salaries and
commissions) represented about 16 percent of the total cost. Utilities,
maintenance, taxes, insurance and depreciation made up the remaining 21 percent.

The average cost of packaging 100 pounds of milled rice in
consumer-size containers was $1.47, (Table 5-4). The packaging
materials alone represented 68 percent of the total cost of packaging.
Administrative and selling expenses per unit of rice milled tended
to be considerably higher in the mills which packaged the rice in
consumer-size packages.

TABLE 5-4. AVERAGE COST PER 100 POUNDS OF PACKAGING MILLED
RICE IN CONSUMER CONTAINERS, 1956-57[1]

Cost item	Cents
Wages and salaries	31.0
Operating expenses[2]	14.6
Depreciation	6.6
Packaging material	94.5
Total	146.7

[1]Nearly 30 percent of the output of mills reporting packaging costs was placed in
consumer packages ranging from 12 ounces to 5 pounds.
[2]Utilities, repairs, maintenance, payroll taxes, etc.

112

TABLE 5-5. AVERAGE FIXED, DIRECT OPERATING AND ALL OTHER COSTS PER 100 POUNDS OF ROUGH RICE MILLED, 1956-57 MILLING SEASON

Size of mill	Average fixed costs	Average operating costs	Other costs	Total costs
	— — — — — — Cents — — — — — —			
Rough rice milled per year				
Less than 400,000 cwt.	13.0	34.9	51.6	99.5
400,000 to 800,000 cwt.	11.4	29.7	53.2	94.3
Over 800,000 cwt.	11.7	26.3	57.5	95.5

Fixed costs varied little among different size groups of mills, ranging from 11 to 13 cents per 100 pounds of rough rice, (Table 5-5).

Direct operating costs (labor, repairs, utilities, etc.) were 35 cents per 100 pounds for small mills, 30 cents for medium-sized mills and 26 cents for large mills.

Analysis of the services rendered and their effect on direct operating costs reveals that the most important factors in explaining variations in cost among mills are the scale of milling and packaging operations, (Table 5-6). On the average, volume of milling operation alone explained 49 percent of variations in this cost category. The proportion of rice packed in consumer-size containers explained an additional 23 percent of the variations in direct operating costs—or about 72 percent of the variations from these two factors.

Because of the lack of a uniform system of accounting among rice mills, it is difficult to obtain an exact cost comparison of the various cost items between mills. Furthermore, mills offer different services beyond the simple operations which further complicates analysis of differences in unit cost among mills. Another difficulty

TABLE 5-6. AVERAGE COST OF PROCESSING AND MARKETING 100 POUNDS OF ROUGH RICE, BY SIZE OF MILL (IN 1,000 CWT. MILLED PER YEAR), 1956-57

Cost item	Less than 400	400 - 800	Over 800
Taxes and insurance	4.5	5.8	3.8
Depreciation	8.5	5.6	7.9
Salaries and wages to production workers	25.5	21.2	19.0
All other salaries and commissions	20.6	19.1	15.2
Plant operating expenses	9.4	8.5	7.3
Selling and general administrative	12.0	14.5	16.9
Outside storage	0.2	2.3	5.0
All packaging material	18.8	17.3	20.4
Total	99.5	94.3	95.5

is to obtain a uniform measure of capacity that would be applicable to all mills when they perform different services. Still another difficulty arises from the fact that some mills may increase or reduce the labor force with changes in output, while others keep a stable force regardless of mill production. Also some mills, usually the smaller ones, may require mill workers to perform other functions not necessarily associated wtih milling operations.

The costs of operating the rice milling business reported by the mills interviewed in this study ranged from $0.97 to $1.39 per barrel, with an average of $1.19.

OBSTACLES TO GREATER EFFICIENCY IN MILL OPERATIONS

Owners of the older mills report that the greatest obstacle to improved efficiency is the time lost (short-time shutdowns) in repairing old equipment. Improper plant layout is another source of inefficiency that is frequently mentioned by owners of the older mills. In addition, mill managers reported that lack of rough rice drying and storage facilities is a major limiting factor to more efficient rough rice procurement. Most mills own drying facilities (only two of the Texas mills do not own rough rice drying facilities). However, most mills have facilities for drying and storing only a small portion of their total rough rice requirements.

Some mills stated that lack of favorable markets or demand for output prevented them from fuller utilization of their milling facilities. Others blamed old buildings and facilities and improper layout of equipment and machinery. A few placed the blame on the government, especially the policy of holding up purchases to keep prices down during harvest when a sizeable volume of clean rice should move to prevent storage facilities from filling up.

Concerning plans of management to remedy the factors that prevent fuller utilization of milling facilities or the major bottleneck in obtaining greater output, one mill will double its rough rice receiving and storage capacity and install additional clean rice storage bins within a year. This same mill plans to go into specialized, precooked rice dishes and mixes, and to upgrade the quality of the present product. Another mill will install new paddy machines and rice grading and sorting equipment in the mill and new drying equipment in their parboiling plant.

Another mill is forming its own export sales department and plans to increase foreign market activities. Increased efforts at advertising and merchandising their own private brands is the goal of another.

114

ROUGH RICE PROCUREMENT AND PRICING PROBLEMS

It is difficult to obtain precise measures of pricing efficiencies in rough rice marketing. Sometimes there is very little relationship between grade, or quality and prices offered. Some mills for example are interested in bidding only on rice of the highest quality while other mills, because of the intended use or nature of their market for the end product, look primarily for lower quality rough rice at a bargain price. In addition, many millers feel that the government, through its price support program, sets the ceiling as well as the floor on rough rice prices and also establishes the level of clean rice prices through its purchase activities and has a strong effect on the world price.

Use of Federal Grades

Although federal grades and standards are established for rough rice, they are not used extensively by Texas and Louisiana mills in procurement operations.

Millers gave several reasons for not using federal grades. Most reasons centered around the feeling of discrepancies between rough rice grades and actual milling outturn. Total milling and head rice yields are apparently the dominant factors in the determination of prices that millers will pay for the several varieties and types. The quality attributes involving broken kernels, heat and otherwise damaged kernels, pecks, red or black rice and weed and other seeds and foreign matter are of lesser importance.

Some millers feel that federal grades are unrealistic, unreliable and unrelated to actual clean rice grades, while others stated simply that government grades are not coordinated with actual results in the milling process. Other mills reported that they trust their own graders more than government graders or that while federal grades are intended for an average of all mills in the industry their buyers' estimates are more accurate for their individual mill. Still others stated that they want to know the quality and milling efficiency (mill outturn) that their mill can obtain with each lot of rice.

Some of the suggestions offered by mills include:

1. Better trained, better qualified and closer supervised grading personnel.

2. Adoption of a universally accepted peck, heat, smut, chalk and related damage grade on a percentage basis.

3. Adoption of a universally accepted count and identification of seeds, red rice and other foreign matter and milling yield on a percentage basis.

4. Adoption of more stringent quality grading; too many lots of rough rice are graded U. S. No. 1 that are actually No. 2 or even No. 3 in quality.

Although most buyers use a sample mill to help determine quality, the human element is still a large factor in grade determination. Depending upon the end use intended, millers probably look at grade factors in more detail than do federal graders. Therefore, most larger mills have developed their own grades based upon the value to them of the various quality attributes. In the final analysis, the miller usually knows what he is buying from a quality standpoint after he has rubbed and examined the rough rice, but in most instances the farmer does not know what he is selling from a quality standpoint. To the average farmer his rice always "looks" better than another lot of the same quality!

Although the existing federal grades are not entirely compatible with the value attributes of rice as seen from the vantage point of millers, there is considerable evidence to suggest that these grades are not used as much as they might be by farmers. At present, farmers use federal grades mostly in obtaining Commodity Credit Corporation loans. Increased use of federal grades could occur if farmers had a better comprehension of the values of the several quality attributes of rice which are considered in the existing grading system.

It is evident that improvements are needed in the rough rice grading system to the end of obtaining official quality designation that will be more compatible with the way millers value rough rice when they buy. The main requirement for change appears to consist of some method of including factors that will more accurately reflect milling yields in the federal grading system.

New U. S. Standards for Rice and Their Implications

U. S. standards for rough, brown and milled rice were revised by the USDA during 1967 and became effective January 1, 1968. This action followed discussions with producers, processors, merchandisers and trade organizations and was taken after considering the suggestions for changes and the views and recommendations of all concerned. This is the first major revision since August 1961.

Basically, the revisions in the standards comprise the following six factors.

1. Classify rice on the basis of size and shape of the kernel (short, medium and long) rather than on variety.

2. Add one new separate grade factor—the amount of paddy (unhulled) kernels—to the standards for brown rice. Under the previous standards, the amount of paddy kernels was not indicated separately from the total amount of seeds and heat damaged kernels.

3. Reduce the moisture content permitted in all numerical grades of milled rice from 15 to 14 percent.

4. Add a factor analysis on the quality of large broken pieces when milling yield is shown on the grade certificate for rough rice.

5. Raise the amount of chalky kernels allowed in all medium grain rough and milled rice to that permitted in medium grain milled rice grown in California, (ranging from 2 percent for U. S. No. 1 to 15 percent for U. S. No. 5) and thus provide a more uniform classification for medium grain rice.

6. Increase the maximum limits for the following factors at the grade levels indicated.

(a) "Red rice and damaged kernels" in grades U. S. Nos. 3 and 4 of the rough rice standards and of the whole head milled rice standards.

(b) "Seeds and heat-damaged kernels" in grade U. S. No. 4 in the milled rice standards.

The remainder of the revisions concerns primarily refinements and clarification of definitions. See Table 5-7.

The stated purposes of the revision in the standards are to more accurately describe the product and to provide a more meaningful and useful yardstick of quality. The revised standards should contribute materially to achieving those objectives provided they are adhered to by all segments of the industry and are accepted and used by both producers and millers.

The limits and interpretation of moisture content, the amount of damaged kernels, and the amount of chalky kernels (all major factors in grade determination) are modernized and improved under the new standards. The new method of classification according to length of grain rather than variety is also expected to help the position of U. S. rice in foreign markets, since the rice of other nations is generally classified as long, medium or short grain.

Reductions in the moisture content of milled rice from 15 to 14 percent in all numerical grades will result in improving the keeping quality since rice with a lower moisture content will store safely for longer periods. This will also bring the moisture content of milled rice in line with the moisture allowed in brown and rough rice.

Indicating the quality or true value of large brokens on the grade certificate for rough rice as a factor in milling yield will enable buyers to have better knowledge of the rice they are purchasing without seeing it or drawing a sample. Likewise, changing the amount of chalky kernels allowed should provide a more uniform classification for medium grain rice.

117

TABLE 5-7. U.S. STANDARDS FOR ROUGH RICE, MAXIMUM LIMITS OF

Grade	Seeds and heat-damaged kernels		Red rice and damaged kernels (singly or combined)	Chalky kernels		Rice of other classes[1]	Color requirements
	Total (singly or combined)	Heat-damaged kernels and objectionable seeds (singly or combined)		In long grain rice	In short and medium grain rice		
	No. in 500 grams		– – – – – – – – – – – – – – – – – Percent – – – – – – – – – – – –				
U.S. no. 1	2	1	0.5	1.0	2.0	1.0	Shall be white or creamy.
U.S. no. 2	4	2	1.5	2.0	4.0	2.0	May be slightly gray.
U.S. no. 3	7	5	2.5	4.0	6.0	3.0	May be light gray.
U.S. no. 4	20	15	4.0	6.0	8.0	5.0	May be gray or slightly rosy.
U.S. no. 5	30	25	6.0	10.0	10.0	10.0	May be dark gray or rosy.
U.S. no. 6	75	75	15.0[2]	15.0	15.0	10.0	May be dark gray or rosy.

U.S. sample grade shall be rough rice which does not meet the requirements for any of the grades from U.S. No. 1 to U.S. No. 6, inclusive; or which contains more than 14.0 percent of moisture; or which is musty, or sour, or heating; or which has any commercially objectionable foreign color; or which is otherwise of distinctly low quality.

[1] These limits do not apply to the class Mixed Rough Rice.
[2] The rice in grade U.S. No. 6 may contain not more than 6.0 percent of damaged kernels.

118

Increasing the maximum limits of such specific grading factors as red rice, damaged and heat-damaged kernels, weed seeds and paddy kernels should provide more proportional intervals or limits between the various grades for those factors and thus be more meaningful as yardsticks of quality.

Cost of Purchasing Rough Rice

Since federal grades and standards are not used, the prevailing system is to sample and evaluate every individual producer lot of rough rice and buy on a bid basis at numerous and scattered sales locations. This system results in costly procurement operation of millers, high storage costs and complicates identification of farm level demand conditions in the rough rice market.

In the absence of a uniform quality evaluating system, little commingling of rough rice exists before it is purchased by mills and purchases are made on relatively small lots. The producer identity is preserved on virtually all rice marketed in Texas and Louisiana. Consequently, the cost of procurement is appreciably above what it might be if individual producer lots could be commingled and if millers could buy in larger lots.

The estimated cost of purchasing rough rice reported by mills interviewed in Texas *and* Louisiana ranged from 4 to 15 cents per barrel, with an average of 8.3 cents per barrel for the eight mills reporting.[2] The average size lot purchased by individual mills ranged from 1,000 to 2,500 barrels.

Mills purchasing lots of rice averaging less than 2,000 barrels (average size—1,433 barrels) incurred an average procurement cost of 10 cents per barrel, while mills purchasing lots averaging more than 2,000 barrels (average size—2,220 barrels) reported an average purchasing cost of 7.2 cents per barrel. This relationship between the average size lot of rough rice purchased and the cost of purchasing rough rice indicates that significant savings could be obtained through adoption of a uniform quality designation system which would allow commingling of rough rice into larger, even-running lots at the producer level.

The mill operators interviewed employed an average of five rough rice buyers, ranging from three to seven per mill. During the 1966-67 season these mills processed 12.7 million barrels of rough rice, or an average of 1.6 million barrels per mill. Assuming that the number of barrels milled during the season represents the volume of rough rice purchased, this represents an average of 299,000 barrels per rough rice buyer employed by the mills reporting. On an indi-

---

[2]Texas Mills reported an estimated cost ranging from 4 to 8 cents per barrel, with an average of 6.5 cents for the mills reporting.

vidual mill basis the volume per buyer ranged from 116,000 to 477,000 barrels. The corresponding cost of purchasing rough rice reported by these two mills was 10 cents for the former and 4 cents for the latter (the lowest of any mill). The average size lots reported were 1,000 and 2,000 barrels, respectively.

The above indicates that there is a definite relationship between the average size lot of rough rice purchased as well as the volume of rice processed or purchased per rough rice buyer employed and the cost of purchasing rough rice. However, only two mills indicated they could obtain savings in their cost of buying rough rice if the size of the average lot was increased. One of these mills reported an estimated saving of about 1 cent per barrel. The other one of the larger mills requiring high-quality rice for its branded, parboiled rice, stated that they could reduce the cost of purchasing rough rice by 50 percent by buying in larger lots (of 10,000 barrels) if it is uniformly blended to a standard grade. This mill reported an average cost of 9 cents per barrel in purchasing its rough rice supplies under present conditions. Two other mills reported that if they had their choice the optimum size lot they would like to obtain from the standpoint of minimizing their procurement cost is 10,000 barrels, and a third mill reported 5,000 barrels as the optimum size. Last year the average size lot purchased by these three mills was 2,088, 1,800 and 1,900 barrels, respectively.

There is also an inverse relationship between total rice milled during one season and the average cost of purchasing rough rice reported by mills interviewed. Mills processing less than two million hundredweights reported an average procurement cost of 8.9 cents per barrel, while those milling more than two million hundredweight had an average cost of 6.1 cents per barrel.

Quality Requirements of Mills and Commingling

Specific measurements of quality factors required by mills are very difficult to obtain and analyze. In most cases the tolerances allowed, as well as the price differentials, or dockage depend upon the purposes or intended use of the rough rice. If, for example, a mill is bidding on a lot of rice which it intends to dispose of under P.L. 480, quality specifications required and tolerances allowed are usually much more lenient than if the mill is purchasing rice to mill and market under its own packaged quality brand. Likewise, rice intended for parboiling may demand certain attributes that are not so crucial if it is to be milled by the conventional method: the degree of peckiness is an example. On the other hand, broken kernels in the hull is not as great a quality factor in rice intended for parboiling as it is in conventional milling since such kernels will usually reseal themselves into a whole grain during the parboiling process.

As indicated previously, with most mills total milling and head rice yields are still the dominant factors in price determination for the several varieties and types—with broken, heat or otherwise damaged kernels, pecks, red or black rice, and weed and other seeds and foreign matter being of lesser importance.

For white-milled rice, mills on the average allocate 70 percent of the value to the yield factor and 30 percent to the several grade factors, and for parboiling the allocation is closer to 60 percent to yield and 40 percent to grade factors.

Mills generally do their own commingling of lots of rough rice before milling at the mill. Concerning the major factors considered and tolerances allowed in commingling, all mills reported that under no circumstance do they commingle different varieties or types. Some mills even keep the first and second crops separate. In commingling lots of the same variety, the reported tolerance on yield ranges from 2½ to 6 pounds per barrel.

Some of the responses to grade factors and tolerances in commingling rough rice include: no mixing of seedy, red or heat-damaged rice with clean rice; commingling is done only within the tolerances of each numerical grade; rice intended for the same use only is commingled, dependent on if it is U. S. No. 1 packaged rice or No. 5 for the government; no tolerance on moisture nor on length-width (uniformity) of grain; milling yield must be within 4 pounds, and peck, red rice and smut within .3 of 1 percent.

Rough Rice Ownership and Risk

Only two rice mills in Texas do not own rough rice drying facilities, and only one does not have rough rice storage facilities. Mills reported an average drying capacity of 13,000 barrels per day. These mills dried an average of 230,000 barrels during 1966 but milled an average of 1,870,000 barrels. The rough rice storage capacity of Texas mills averages 502,000 barrels—with a range from 250,000 to 2 million barrels. In some mills the total volume of rice normally stored during the season is several times the milling capacity since they perform "in-and-out" storage operations.

Ownership and storage of rough rice supplies reduces the trouble and difficulty of procurement during the latter part of the milling season. However, there is the element of risk and uncertainty of price changes in ownership of rough rice. Evidently, most mills feel that the security of having rough rice supplies available when needed outweighs the risk and uncertainty of future price changes, or that the clean rice market will advance more than the rough rice market. Mills reported obtaining from 50 to 95 percent of their yearly rice supply at time of harvest with only two mills reported purchasing rough rice in sizeable quantities after December 31.

121

At harvest time there is the advantage of wider selection and better quality which are important factors to mills requiring higher quality rice for their private brands of package rice. Mills requiring top quality rough rice seldom pass up an opportunity to bid on a lot meeting their requirements when it is offered for sale.

The chances for a price rise from time of harvest to January are better than eight to one. Thus, there is an attractive speculative element involved in buying green rice during the harvesting period and storing it until it is milled in anticipation of a price increase.

A comparison was made of the seasonal movement of average prices received by farmers for rough rice in Arkansas, Louisiana and Texas for the 5-year period 1961-62 to 1965-66 (as reported by USDA quarterly report, *Consumer and Marketing Service—*18, 1966). The data on Tables 5-8a, 8b and 8c indicate that for those years the peak seasonal advance in prices to producers occurred in March in Texas, in April in Louisiana and in February in Arkansas. The average advance in price above August amounted to 78 cents per barrel in Texas, 93 cents in Louisiana and $1.02 above the September average price in Arkansas.

This compares, for example, with the storage charges reported by Texas firms of 30 cents from harvest to April 30. To this should be added the cost of ownership of the rough rice at approximately 5 cents per month, or 45 cents.

There are several reasons advanced for the drop in producer prices during the latter part of the season, beginning in April in Texas and May in Louisiana. However, the main reasons for this situation are, first, that at that time many mills are beginning to shut down for the year and are not disposed to purchase rough rice; second, a large proportion of the mills that plan to continue operating through July usually have already acquired the volume of rice they intend to process; and, third, seed rice which has not been planted is offered for sale resulting in an unbalanced situation between the quantity of rough rice available and the active demand by mills. For the 5-year period, 1961-65, the yearly carryover stocks of rough rice amounted to an average of 1.4 million hundredweight for the southern states and 1.7 million hundredweight for the United States as a whole.

SUMMARY

Forty-six mills operated in the two states of Texas and Louisiana in 1962 but only 26 in 1967. This reduction in the number of mills results from the fact that (1) small, independent, family owned and operated huller mills have been forced out of business by high operating costs and increasing competition for rough rice supplies and clean

TABLE 5-8a. MONTHLY AVERAGE PRICES RECEIVED BY FARMERS FOR ROUGH RICE FOR THE FIVE-YEAR PERIOD 1961-62 TO 1965-66 IN TEXAS

	Aug.	Sept.	Oct.	Nov.	Dec.	Jan.	Feb.	March	April	May	June	July
						Cents per 100 pounds						
Price	489	493	505	519	510	526	524	538	534	526	518	524
Difference from previous month	—	+4	+12	+14	−9	+16	−2	+14	−4	−8	−8	+6
Accrued difference	—	+4	+16	+30	+21	+37	+35	+49	+45	+37	+29	+35
Difference per barrel (cents)		6.4	25.6	48.0	33.6	59.2	56.0	78.4	72.0	59.2	46.4	56.0

TABLE 5-8b. MONTHLY ROUGH RICE PRICE DIFFERENTIALS IN LOUISIANA

	Aug.	Sept.	Oct.	Nov.	Dec.	Jan.	Feb.	March	April	May	June	July
						Cents per 100 pounds						
Price	470	479	500	504	515	522	524	526	528	512	506	487
Difference from previous month	—	+9	+21	+4	+11	+7	+2	+4	+2	−16	−6	−19
Accrued difference	—	+9	+30	+34	+45	+52	+52	+56	+58	+42	+36	+17
Difference per barrel (cents)		14.4	48.0	54.4	72.0	83.2	83.2	89.6	92.8	67.2	57.6	27.2

TABLE 5-8c. MONTHLY ROUGH RICE PRICE DIFFERENTIALS IN ARKANSAS

	Sept.	Oct.	Nov.	Dec.	Jan.	Feb.	March	April	May	June	July
						Cents per 100 pounds					
Price	466	503	519	526	528	530	530	530	530	530	524
Difference from previous month	—	+37	+16	+7	+2	+2					−6
Accrued difference	—	+37	+53	+60	+62	+64	64	64	64	64	+58
Difference per barrel (cents)		59.2	84.8	96.0	99.2	102.4	102.4	102.4	102.4	102.4	92.8

rice markets and (2) large, multi-unit firms have closed their smaller inefficient mills and consolidated into larger, centrally located, more efficient milling operations.

There also has been some horizontal integration in the rice milling industry during the past few years. This has taken place through mergers, acquisition and consolidation of several milling units under one management. The milling industry in Texas and Louisiana is likely to become more concentrated in the future.

The trend toward integration and increased consolidation will no doubt continue as mills strive for increased economies of scale and compete more strenuously in the clean rice market. Further, increased capacity and efficiency through improvements in plant and facilities can be achieved only by sizable capital outlays. The magnitude of capital requirements for equipment and facilities and to finance rough rice inventories will make it more difficult for small rice mill operators to compete effectively in the future.

Approximately 75 percent of the rice milled in Texas during 1967 was packed in 100-pound bags, about 9 percent was packed in either 25 or 50-pound bags, 4 percent was sold in bulk and about 12 percent was marketed by mills in consumer-size cartons of 5 pounds or less. Texas rice mills have integrated their operations forward toward the consumer to a larger extent than has occurred in Louisiana. However, much of the output in Texas is still marketed in wholesale-type packages or in bulk. In Texas there are only two of the seven mills that do not package milled rice in consumer units and market under their own brand names. In contrast, only five of the nineteen Louisiana mills are operating in this fashion.

Mills in both states depend heavily on export markets with sales abroad accounting for proportions ranging 40 to 99 percent of the total output of individual mills. Only four mills in Texas and the same number in Louisiana engage in direct selling activities in foreign countries. The others sell to large grain exporters and have not developed their own markets or sales outlets in foreign countries. A limiting factor in the development of export marketing operations is that only the larger mills have the capacity or volume which allows them to make offers for government purchases that may be in lots ranging from 10,000 to 50,000 tons.

Owners of older mills indicate that the greatest obstacle to improved efficiency is time lost in repairing old equipment. Improper plant layout is another source of inefficiency that is frequently mentioned by the owners of the older mills. In addition, mill managers indicate that lack of rough rice drying and storage facilities is a major limiting factor to more efficient rough rice procurement. Most mills own drying facilities, but few have capacity for drying and

124

storing the proportion of their total rough rice requirements that they consider necessary for efficient milling operations.

Although federal grades and standards are established for rough rice, they are not used extensively by Texas and Louisiana mills in procurement operations. Rather, the prevailing system is to sample and evaluate individual producer lots of rough rice and to buy on a bid basis at numerous and scattered sales locations. The system results in costly procurement operation of millers, high storage costs, and it complicates identification of farm level demand conditions in the rough rice market.

In the absence of a uniform quality evaluation system, there is little commingling of rough rice before it is purchased by mills. The producer identity is preserved on virtually all rice marketed in Texas and Louisiana. As a result, the cost of procurement is appreciably above what it might be if individual producer lots could be commingled and if millers could buy in larger lots. A brief survey in Texas and Louisiana indicates that mills purchasing lots of rice averaging less than 2,000 barrels incurred procurement costs of 10 cents per barrel while mills purchasing lots averaging more than 2,000 barrels had procurement costs of 7.2 cents per barrel. The inverse relationship between the amount of rough rice purchased per lot and the cost of purchasing indicates that significant savings could be attained through adoption of a quality designation system which would allow consolidation of rough rice into larger lots that moves into storage before it is sold to millers.

There is also an inverse relationship between total rice milled during one season and the average cost of purchasing rough rice reported by mills interviewed. Mills processing less than 2 million hundredweight reported an average procurement cost of 8.9 cents per barrel while those milling more than 2 million hundredweight had an average cost of 6.1 cents per barrel.

Millers gave several reasons for not using federal grades in their procurement operations, most of which centered around their opinion that there were discrepancies between rough rice grades and actual milling outturn. Total milling and head rice yields are apparently the dominant factors in the determination of prices that millers will pay for the several varieties and types of rice. The quality attributes involving broken kernels, heat damage, pecks, red or black rice and foreign matter are of lesser importance. However, U. S. standards for rough rice are based primarily on those factors which mills consider secondary in importance. It is evident that improvements are needed in the grading system to the end of obtaining official quality designations that will be more compatible with the way millers value rough rice when they buy. The main requirement for change appears to consist of some method of including factors that will more accurately reflect milling yields in the federal grading system.

Even though the existing federal grades are not entirely compatible with the value attributes of rice as seen from the vantage point of millers, there is also considerable evidence to suggest that these grades are not used as much as they might be by farmers. At present, the major use that farmers make of federal grades is in obtaining loans under the government price support program. Farmers could become more astute in their marketing decisions through a better comprehension of the values of the several quality attributes of rice which are considered in the existing grading system.

U. S. standards for rough, brown and milled rice were recently revised and became effective on January 1, 1968. These are the first major revisions since 1961. They are intended to describe the product more accurately, and to provide a more meaningful and useful yardstick of quality. The revised standards should contribute materially to achievement of these objectives, provided they are adhered to by all segments of the industry and are used by both producers and millers.

6

Rough Rice Drying And Storage

Harlon D. Traylor
Randall Stelly
Reid M. Grigsby
W. R. Morrison

More than 400 firms are in operation with drying and storage facilities for rough rice in the continental United States.[1] Arkansas has over 125 firms engaged in drying and storing rice. The storage capacity for rough rice handled by these organizations ranges from about 19,000 hundredweight to over 1 million hundredweight. Cooperatives handle over 60 percent of the total drying and storing of rough rice in Arkansas. About 20 organizations supply the off-farm drying and storage facilities for rice in California with the majority of them equipped to handle volume production. Storage capacity of these firms ranges from 47,500 hundredweight to over 3.3 million hundredweight of rice. Cooperative associations dry one-fourth of the total rice produced in California. In Louisiana and Texas, about 220 firms dry and store rough rice. The number of firms is about equally divided between the two states with storage capacities ranging from about 16,000 to over 560,000 hundredweight of rough rice. Over 40 percent of the rice produced in these states is dried and stored by cooperative associations.

The importance to rice growers and others of efficient, low cost drying and storage of rough rice is reflected in the amount expended for these services. Of the $200 million received in 1966 for rough rice by growers in Louisiana and Texas for example, an estimated $12 million, or 6 percent of the value, was spent for artificial drying. The cost of storage though not generally borne as directly by growers, probably amounted to another $5 million.[2]

LOUISIANA AND TEXAS

The amount of rough rice dried by on-farm facilities, off-farm facilities and green rice facilities at mills in Louisiana and Texas in

---

[1] *The Rice Journal,* Directory of U.S. Rice Driers, 1967 Annual Issue.

[2] In this chapter the term "off-farm rough rice drying and storage" will refer to facilities other than those currently milling rice. These facilities normally handle rice for growers and others on a custom basis. Drying facilities connected with mills actively processing rice will be referred to as "green rice facilities at mills" and storage facilities as "rough rice storage at mills."

1966 with comparisons for 1960 is estimated as follows:

Item	1960	1966
	1,000 hundredweight	
On-farm facilities	1,000	5,000
Off-farm facilities	20,000	28,000
Green rice facilities at mills	5,000	9,000
Total	26,000	42,000

These states account for more than half of the nation's rice acreage. Production in the two states increased from 26 to 42 million or 16 million hundredweight between 1960 and 1966. Off-farm facilities operating on a custom basis dried about half of this increase. The rate of growth was not as great for this segment of the industry as for either on-farm facilities or green rice facilities at mills. The latter two types increased drying by about 4 million hundredweight each during this period, with on-farm drying more than quadrupling. Green rice facilities at mills appear to have increased much more rapidly in Louisiana than in Texas.

Harvest Season

The development of an early and relatively short harvest season has greatly affected the industry in recent years. In Texas, for example, 1,884,000 hundredweight of rough rice was received by driers and mills during the second week of September 1960, the peak week.[3] By 1965, some 3,873,000 hundredweight was received in the peak week, the third week of July. This amounts to more than a 100 percent increase in rough rice receipts during the peak week in a period of time when the total crop increased only 70 percent.

Louisiana facilities have faced a similar situation. In the peak week of 1965 some 20 percent of the harvest arrived at mills and driers, compared to about 15 percent during the peak week in the earlier years of the decade.[4] The peak week also changed to the third week of August from the second week of September.

In large part this phenomenon has been due to the adoption by growers of new varieties of rice and of more precise cultural practices. For example, some 18 million hundredweight of Bluebonnet rice was harvested in the main rice producing states in 1960 as compared to only 16 million in 1965, while the Nato variety increased from 10 million to 26 million hundredweight.[5] Other varieties, some of which

[3]Welsh, Delane E., *Impact of Yield and Acreage Changes on Rice Drying and Storage Facilities in Texas*, MP-862, Texas Agricultural Experiment Station, Texas A&M University, College Station, Texas, January 1968.

[4]United States Department of Agriculture, AMS, Grain Division, *Rice Market News Supplement Rough Rice Receipts*, (processed), New Orleans, Louisiana.

[5]*Rice Situation*, RS-10, ERS, USDA, Washington, D. C., January 1966.

were not even grown commercially at that time, have increased in a similar manner. These varieties include Belle Patna, the Roses, Nova and Saturn; production of Toro, Rexora, Century Patna, Zenith and Magnolia have decreased drastically.

For custom and green rice drying facilities at mills, the shorter harvest season has meant that more facilities were needed per unit of rice, tending to increase the cost per unit of rough rice dried relative to that of on-farm stationary facilities which were little affected by this advent. Some operators of custom facilities contend that charges that can be obtained for drying and storage are not now sufficient to build additional facilities for any but regular customers.

Mill operators, on the other hand, and especially those in Louisiana, seem rather eager to expand drying facilities. One logical advantage in having more green rice facilities at mills is the possibility of saving one hauling and one handling between the farmer and the mill. Another is to earn the drying and storage charges. Still another is a savings in rice drying and storage costs that may be obtained by commingling ownership lots as it is dried as compared to the more conventional system of buying dried rice, the ownership identity of which has been preserved until purchased by mills.

Many producers feel that mills profit greatly by purchasing green rice because the market is somewhat less competitive than is the case for the more conventional system of buying dried rice. They feel also that those who hold rice after drying for later use or sale earn rather large profits. However, the price incentive to storage, appears adequate but not substantial (Figure 6-1). A current bottleneck apparently lies in receiving and drying rough rice. It seems obvious that off-farm driers must find economical ways to let their customers cut rice when it is ready and to receive the rice without keeping the growers' trucks in line for unduly long waits before unloading. Some driers could improve their operations in this respect with little added cost.[6] A potential development that might allow custom driers to operate at less cost and improve the quality of the rice dried is infrared energy.[7]

During the late summer and early autumn of 1967, 11 operators of custom drying and storage facilities in Louisiana and Texas were questioned concerning possible adjustment problems and solutions

[6]See for example, Calderwood, David. "Use of Aeration for Maintaining Quality of Undried Rice," *Proceedings, Eleventh Rice Technical Working Groups,* University of California, Division of Agricultural Sciences, 1.1, 3-167VL.

[7]Wratten, F. T. and M. D. Faulkner, "New System for Rice Drying," *Proceedings, Eleventh Rice Technical Working Group,* Universtiy of California, Division of Agricultural Sciences, 1.1, 3-167VL.

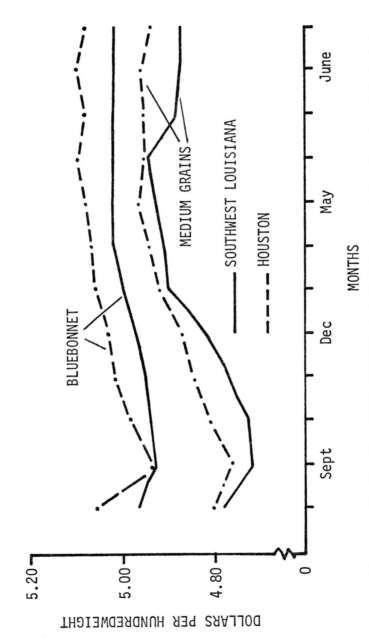

Figure 6-1. Average Monthly Prices, 1962-67, FOB Mills, U. S. No. 2 Grade, Rough Rice Equivalent of Head Rice.[1]

[1]Based on 50 pounds of head rice per 100 pounds of rough rice for the Bluebonnet variety and 57 pounds of head rice per 100 pounds of rough rice for the medium grain varieties.

Source: *Rice, Annual Market Summary*, 1967, C&MS-18, (1967), USDA, Washington, D.C.

in the drying and storage industry of their states. Six of these were located in Louisiana and 5 in Texas.

Some of the operators surveyed contend that if rice could be handled on a commingled basis, small lots would command as high a price as large lots. In the summer and fall of 1967 some millers confirmed they could reduce their purchasing costs if they could obtain large lots.

The Louisiana Agricultural Experiment Station is currently investigating the relationship of rough rice prices to size of lot sold, while holding several other important factors constant.

The operators also firmly contend that they could dry rice at considerably less cost if allowed by growers to commingle lots of like variety and quality without regard to ownership. With the same facilities and practically the same amount of labor and other costs, Louisiana operators claim they could increase their drying capacity an average of 18 percent and storage by 24 percent; Texas operators by 26 and 23 percent, respectively. Under the present system of maintaining ownership identity on nearly every lot of rice dried, bin capacity is very often only partly used. Moreover, the "down time" of the drying units could be reduced considerably if it were not necessary to clean out the drying units between lots. Commingling, however, raises a number of important questions where it has not been practiced to any great extent before. More problems are involved in commingling green rice than dried rice but they can be solved.

DRYING AND STORAGE COSTS

A 1959-62 study provides much insight on drying and storage costs in Louisiana and Texas.[8] In this study the four main types of rough rice drying and storage facilities were analyzed. Three of these were on-farm units and consisted of (1) round bulk bins, (2) buildings with bulk bins and (3) multipass, continuous-flow units. All off-farm facilities studied were multipass, continuous-flow type units. Altogether, some 95 units were studied intensively over the 3-year period. Rough rice drying and storage operations by millers were not included in the analysis.

Major factors considered in appraising the various types of facilities were in-plant operating costs, marketing costs and quality considerations.

Operating Costs

Operating costs are summarized into two groups, variable and fixed. Variable costs are those which vary with output. Fixed costs

[8]Traylor, Harlon D., Clyde B. Markeson and Carter Price, *Costs of Drying and Storing Rough Rice in Louisiana and Texas,* Marketing Research Report No. 799, USDA, Washington, D. C., July 1967.

TABLE 6-1. ALL ON-FARM FACILITIES: OPERATING COSTS PER HUN-
DREDWEIGHT OF DRIED ROUGH RICE, BY TYPE OF FACILITY, LOUISI-
ANA AND TEXAS, 1959-61

	Facility			
Cost item	Round bulk bins	Building with bulk bins	Multi-pass	Average or total
	— — — — — Cents per cwt. — — — — —			
Variable				
Labor	2.8	4.5	4.2	3.9
Spray and fumigants	0.4	0.4	0.1	0.3
Fuel	1.3	0.4	2.1	1.4
Repairs	1.4	0.5	1.3	1.1
Electricity	4.0	5.1	1.8	3.3
Grain insurance	0.2	0.2	0.3	0.2
Other	0.8	1.1	1.4	1.1
Total	10.9	12.2	11.2	11.3
Fixed				
Depreciation	15.6	21.1	10.2	14.8
Insurance	1.6	2.6	2.3	2.2
Taxes	2.4	3.3	1.6	2.3
Interest	9.8	13.2	6.2	9.2
Total	29.4	40.2	20.3	28.5
Grand total	40.3	52.4	31.5	39.8
Number of observations	102	78	42	222
Number of facilities	34	26	14	74
Average cost of facilities (dollars)	14,762	29,519	38,671	24,454
Average capacity (cwt.)	6,761	11,495	39,979	14,709
Average output (cwt.)	4,519	6,709	18,712	7,974

are those which would be incurred even if there were no output. For
those considering constructing new facilities, both variable and fixed
costs are relevant. Variable costs are more relevant to those already
owning facilities.

Total operating costs for drying in all on-farm units averaged
40 cents per hundredweight of dried rice (Table 6-1). Buildings with
bulk bins had the highest cost (52 cents), followed by round bulk bins
(40 cents) and multipass facilities (32 cents). These differences
resulted chiefly from the relative importance of fixed costs, which
accounted for 77 percent of the total costs for buildings with bulk
bins, 73 percent for round bulk bins and 65 percent for multipass
driers.

Operating cost per hundredweight generally declined as the
volume of rice dried increased from 50 percent or less to 80 percent
or more of drier capacity. For example, round bulk bin facilities
operating at 50 percent or less of capacity averaged 69 cents per
hundredweight dried, while those operating at 80 percent or more
averaged 32 cents (Table 6-2).

132

Operating costs for off-farm units were allocated to drying, storing and services by management representatives of each of the commercial facilities. Those costs that would not have been incurred had only drying and storage been performed were allocated to services. Next, that part of the remaining costs that would not have been incurred had only rice drying been performed was allocated to storage. The remaining costs were assigned to the drying operation. Based on these reports, average variable and fixed costs per hundredweight were estimated.

Facilities operating at 80 percent or more of capacity experienced considerably lower costs than those operating at lower capacities (Table 6-3). Compared with on-farm facilities, however, a larger proportion of the off-farm facilities were operated near capacity levels.

Storage Costs

Most operators of on-farm facilities reported little or no additional operation cost for storage over that already incurred for drying. However, operators of off-farm units did report additional costs

TABLE 6-2. ROUND BULK BINS: OPERATING COSTS PER HUNDRED-WEIGHT OF DRIED ROUGH RICE, BY PERCENTAGE OF CAPACITY USED, LOUISIANA AND TEXAS, 1959-61

Cost item	Percentage of capacity used			Average or total
	50 or less	51 - 79	80 or more	
	— — — — — Cents per cwt. — — — — —			
Variable				
Labor	2.7	2.7	2.8	2.8
Sprays and fumigants	0.6	0.7	0.3	0.4
Fuel	1.4	1.0	1.4	1.3
Repairs	1.9	1.5	1.2	1.4
Electricity	6.2	5.9	2.6	4.0
Grain insurance	0.2	0.2	0.2	0.2
Other	0.7	1.1	0.7	0.8
Total	13.7	13.1	9.2	10.9
Fixed				
Depreciation	29.2	15.3	12.1	15.6
Insurance	3.0	1.3	1.3	1.6
Taxes	4.6	2.4	1.9	2.4
Interest	18.3	9.5	7.6	9.8
Total	55.1	28.5	22.9	29.4
Grand total	68.8	41.6	32.1	40.3
Number of observations	36	27	39	102
Number of facilities	1	1	1	34
Average capacity (cwt.)	6,692	6,317	7,112	6,761
Average output (cwt.)	1,997	4,183	7,007	4,519

[1]Some facilities operated at different levels from one year to the next.

TABLE 6-3. OFF-FARM DRIERS: OPERATING COSTS PER HUNDRED-WEIGHT OF DRIED ROUGH RICE, BY PERCENTAGE OF DRYING CAPACITY USED, LOUISIANA AND TEXAS, 1959-61

Cost item	Percentage of capacity used			Average or total
	50 or less	51 - 79	80 or more	
	— — — — — Cents per cwt. — — — — —			
Variable				
Wages and salaries	10.6	14.7	12.7	13.4
Utilities	3.0	1.9	2.3	2.2
Grain insurance	0.8	0.5	0.6	0.6
Repairs	1.5	1.4	1.3	1.3
Administrative	1.0	1.2	1.2	1.2
Other	2.6	0.7	1.0	0.9
Total	19.5	20.4	19.1	19.6
Fixed				
Depreciation	10.8	6.4	6.3	6.4
Interest	8.1	6.6	4.4	5.2
Taxes	1.5	1.2	1.0	1.1
Insurance	1.0	1.2	1.5	1.4
Total	21.4	15.4	13.2	14.1
Grand total	40.9	35.8	32.3	33.7
Less miscellaneous drying income	1.0	1.0	1.0	1.0
Net costs	39.9	34.8	31.3	32.7
Number of observations	4	23	36	63
Number of facilities	1	1	1	21
Average capacity (cwt.)	97,337	220,102	220,084	212,297
Average output (cwt.)	45,208	155,340	196,483	171,858

[1]Some facilities operated at different levels from one year to the next.

averaging 21 cents a hundredweight dried (Table 6-4). As volume stored increased from 50 percent or less of capacity to 80 percent or more, average costs per hundredweight decreased from 24 cents to 10 cents.

Marketing Costs

Growers have, in addition to operating or in-plant expenses of drying and storage, certain other important costs, many of which vary with the marketing method used and with whether rice is stored on farms or in commercial units (Table 6-5). Such costs, grouped here as "marketing costs," include charges by sales agencies, hauling and handling expenses, contributions for market development, cost of grain insurance during storage, interest on the amount invested in grain, losses from shrinkage and costs associated with government loans under the price-support program.

Total Costs

Table 6-6 summarizes average total costs to growers in 1959-62 for drying, storing and marketing rough rice over the 3-year period, by type of facility and marketing system used.

TABLE 6-4. OFF-FARM DRIERS: OPERATING COSTS PER HUNDRED-WEIGHT OF STORED ROUGH RICE, BY PERCENTAGE OF STORAGE CAPACITY USED, LOUISIANA AND TEXAS, 1959-61

Cost item	Percentage of capacity used			Average or total
	50 or less	51 - 79	80 or more	
	— — — — — Cents per cwt. — — — — —			
Variable				
Wages and salaries	6.7	2.3	[1]	5.5
Utilities	1.0	0.6	0.2	0.8
Repairs	0.9	0.2	0.1	0.8
Administrative	0.8	0.6	0.4	0.7
Other	1.8	1.7	0.1	1.7
Total	11.2	5.4	0.8	9.5
Fixed				
Depreciation	6.9	3.3	4.5	6.2
Interest	4.9	2.1	4.0	4.4
Taxes	1.0	0.4	0.7	0.9
Insurance	1.1	0.3	0.8	0.9
Total	13.9	6.1	10.0	12.4
Grand total	25.1	11.5	10.8	21.9
Less miscellaneous storage income	1.0	1.0	1.0	1.0
Net selected costs	24.1	10.8	9.8	20.9
Number of observations	56	5	2	63
Number of facilities	[2]	[2]	[2]	21
Average capacity (cwt.)	187,207	166,341	161,704	184,741
Average output (cwt.)	48,193	108,567	152,001	56,281

[1]Less than 0.1 cent per hundredweight.
[2]Numbers were not specified by percentage of capacity used since some facilities operated at different levels from one year to the next.

On the average, round bulk bins operated at 67 percent of their drying capacity, buildings with bulk bins at 58 percent, on-farm multi-pass units at 47 percent and off-farm commercial facilities at 81 percent. Commercial units operated at an average of 30 percent of their storage capacity. Similarly on-farm units made very little use of their storage capacity during this time.

In Table 6-7, average total per unit costs are summarized for those facilities which operated at or above 80 percent of capacity.

Quality Considerations

To compare the quality of rice dried and stored in the various types of facilities, samples were drawn from 494 lots after drying and from 182 lots after storing. Control samples from the same lots were drawn when the rice was still green, and dried in thin layers on screens with natural air. The samples were obtained over the 3-year marketing period, 1959-62.

Differences in both grade and milling yield were determined from U. S. grade certificates obtained for each of the samples. Values were computed by applying price support rates for the qualities shown on the grade certificates. Little difference in average value was found between rice dried in multipass and rice dried in stationary units. Such differences as did exist disappeared after the rice had been stored.

A possible explanation for the disappearance of differences after storage is contained in research findings showing that milling yields increase when rice is stored for more than 3 weeks.[9] In the present

[9]Faulkner, Macon D. and Finis T. Wratten, "Abstracts on Drying and Storage, Summary of Rice Drying Research in Louisiana," *Proceedings, Tenth Rice Technical Working Group,* USDA, ARS, 72-39, October 1965.

TABLE 6-5. MARKETING COSTS PER HUNDREDWEIGHT OF DRIED AND STORED ROUGH RICE, BY MARKETING METHOD USED, AND BY TYPE OF DRIER, LOUISIANA AND TEXAS, 1959-61

Type of drier and cost item	Selling on the open market		Forfeiting grain under government loan program
	After drying	After storage	
Stationary bulk farm bins	— — — — Cents per cwt. — — — —		
Sales agencies	3.1	3.1	
Extra hauling and handling			11.9
Contributions for market development	1.8	1.8	
Grain insurance during storage		1.0	1.0
Grain investment	2.5	10.0	2.5
Shrinkage	2.5	5.0	5.0
Application for government loan		2.0	2.0
Total	9.9	22.9	22.4
Multipass type farm driers			
Sales agencies	3.1	3.1	
Extra hauling and handling			11.9
Contributions for market development	1.8	1.8	
Grain insurance during storage		3.3	3.3
Grain investment	1.2	9.5	1.2
Shrinkage	2.5	5.0	5.0
Application for government loan		2.0	2.0
Total	8.6	24.7	23.4
Off-farm driers			
Sales agencies	3.1	3.1	
Contributions for market development	1.8	1.8	
Grain insurance during storage		3.3	3.3
Grain investment	1.2	9.5	1.2
Shrinkage	2.5	5.0	5.0
Application for government loan		2.0	2.0
Total	8.6	24.7	11.5

study, samples from multipass driers were analyzed for quality within 7 to 14 days after harvest, whereas the samples from stationary type driers were analyzed 21 to 42 days after harvest because of the more gradual drying process. Thus, the slightly poorer milling yield and value of rice from multipass driers at the end of the drying period may have been due to the lack of aging rather than to type of drying facility.

While there was little difference in the average value of rice from the different types of driers, individual lots differed greatly. Possible explanations for such differences are sampling errors, grading errors and differences in the exact operating techniques at particular driers.

After considering the influence of aging on quality and the wide variation among individual samples studied, it was concluded that no significant difference existed in the average quality of rice dried in stationary and multipass facilities. Another conclusion is that this whole matter needs intensive study especially with regard to sampling, grading, determining value and the implications these

TABLE 6-6. AVERAGE TOTAL COSTS PER HUNDREDWEIGHT OF DRYING, STORING AND SELLING ROUGH RICE, BY TYPE OF FACILITY AND MARKETING SITUATION, LOUISIANA AND TEXAS, 1959-61

| Marketing situation and cost item | Type of facility | | | | |
| | On-farm | | Off-farm | | |
	Round bulk bins	Buildings with bulk bins	Multi-pass	Coopera-tive	Other
	— — — — — — Cents per cwt. — — — — — —				
Selling rice immediately after drying					
Drying costs	40.3	52.4	31.5	34.3	28.7
Marketing costs	9.9	9.9	8.6	8.6	8.6
Total	50.2	62.3	40.1	42.9	37.3
Selling rice after storage					
Operating costs					
Drying	40.3	52.4	31.5	34.3	28.7
Storage				18.6	33.2
Marketing costs	22.9	22.9	24.7	24.7	24.7
Total	63.2	75.3	56.2	77.6	86.6
Forfeiting rice under government price-support loan program					
Operating costs					
Drying	40.3	52.4	31.5	34.3	28.7
Storage				18.6	33.2
Marketing costs	22.4	22.4	23.4	11.5	11.5
Total	62.7	74.8	54.9	64.4	73.4

have on farmers' marketing decisions. The methods now used are useful, the best available, and should not be regarded as ineffective. However, the feasibility of an improved system should be explored.

Other Considerations

Because of the relatively large drying capacity of even the smallest farm multipass drier, these driers can be used efficiently only in rather large-scale farm operations. In the sample drawn for this study, all farm multipass driers were classified as large, that is, had a drying capacity of more than 11,340 hundredweight. In some of the situations studied, stationary bin driers were used efficiently in relatively small-scale farm operations. However, the small-scale farm drying and storage facilities tended to be under-utilized by growers, resulting in relatively high unit cost operations. Stationary bin driers with a capacity of 5,000 hundredweight or more seemingly have a much better chance for success.

During the 3-year period studied, prices for Bluebonnet rice rose an average of 29 cents a hundredweight after the harvesting season (Figure 6-2). Considering the uncertainty of seasonal price rises and

TABLE 6-7. AVERAGE TOTAL COSTS PER HUNDREDWEIGHT FOR DRYING, STORING AND SELLING ROUGH RICE, BY TYPE OF FACILITY AND MARKETING SITUATION, FOR PLANTS OPERATING AT 80 PERCENT OR MORE OF CAPACITY, LOUISIANA AND TEXAS, 1959-61

| | Type of facility | | | |
| | On-farm | | | |
Marketing situation and cost item	Round bulk bins	Buildings with bulk bins	Multi-pass	Off-farm
	— — — — — Cents per cwt. — — — — —			
Selling rice immediately after drying				
Drying costs	32.1	41.2	24.9	31.3
Marketing costs	9.9	9.9	8.6	8.6
Total	42.0	51.1	33.5	39.9
Selling rice after storage				
Operating costs				
Drying	32.1	41.2	24.9	31.3
Storage				9.8
Marketing costs	22.9	22.9	24.7	24.7
Total	55.0	64.1	49.6	65.8
Forfeiting rice under government price-support loan program				
Operating costs				
Drying	32.1	41.2	24.9	31.3
Storage				9.8
Marketing costs	22.4	22.4	23.4	11.5
Total	54.5	63.6	48.3	52.6

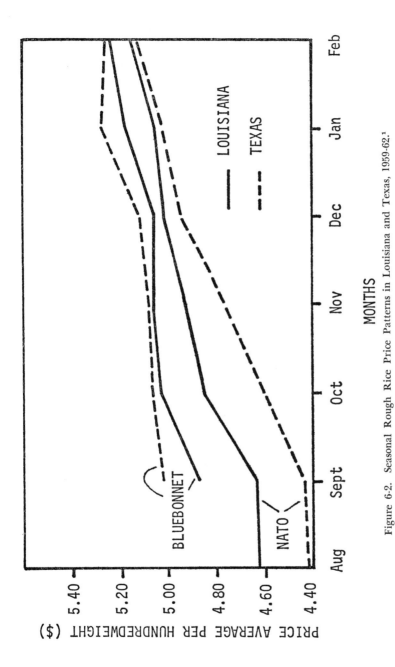

Figure 6-2. Seasonal Rough Rice Price Patterns in Louisiana and Texas, 1959-62.[1]

[1]Based on sales of U. S. No. 1 and 2 grades, FOB mills, with a milling yield of 50 pounds of whole rice and 68 pounds of total rice per 100 pounds of rough rice for the Bluebonnet variety and 57 whole and 69 total per 100 pounds of the Nato variety.

Source: *Rice, Annual Market Summary*, 1962, AMS 277 (1962) USDA, Washington, D.C.

the cost of storing rice, the incentive for storing Bluebonnet rice was not very great at that time. In contrast, the seasonal price rise for the Nato variety averaged about 61 cents a hundredweight, far more than enough to justify the cost of storage as determined by the 1959-62 study. A possible reason that more Nato rice was not stored is the difficulty of drying and storing medium grain rice such as Nato compared with the long grain varieties such as Bluebonnet. Moreover, medium grain rice ordinarily matures somewhat earlier than the long grain varieties, and hence may require more storage time which involves more expense.

Although rice driers consisting of buildings with bulk bins showed the highest drying and storage costs, they have more alternative uses. Should the drying and storage operation be abandoned they can easily be converted into other types of buildings needed on most farms.

On many occasions, commercial driers are unable to receive all the green rice that growers would like to deliver. The threat of a storm, for example, may cause a large number of growers to harvest at the same time in order to minimize field losses. On-farm driers are more likely to have storage space readily available than are commercial driers when a large part of the crop needs to be harvested simultaneously. Rice normally should be harvested at a definite stage of maturity and the drying process needs to begin soon thereafter to avoid loss in quality and yield. During periods of peak harvest, growers' trucks are frequently tied up for a longer period at commercial driers than at on-farm driers.

ARKANSAS AND CALIFORNIA

Commingling rough rice of like variety, milling yield and quality at custom driers has already been widely accepted in California and Arkansas, the other two leading rice producing states in the nation. In the opinion of the writers such facilities have been more nearly able to keep pace with the expansion in production that took place in those states in recent years than in Louisiana and Texas.

In commingling, rice is weighed and tested for moisture while green. From these data, poundage is calculated for the rice after being dried to a safe storage level (Table 6-8). Because of shrinkage other than moisture, the facility responsible for weights also deducts an additional one to two percent as a safety factor. The actual amount of shrinkage above that calculated for moisture varies among other factors with the cleaning and other facilities of the particular drier and the kind of rice delivered to it.

Operators of some of these driers estimate grade and milling yield from green samples, and growers readily accept such determinations.

Other operators use a more elaborate system in which green samples are dried in a sample drier before yield and quality determinations are made. Some rely on government grade factors while others use similar but not necessarily the same factors. Efficiency of rice marketing in this regard could be improved considerably by the development of an official government grade for green rice.

Differentials established by the government price support loan program for variety, milling yield and grade are used by some operators to appraise differences in value based on quality. Others use a slightly different but similar system.

Farmer cooperative mills in Arkansas and California operating commingled rice pools advance about 75 percent of the support price to growers at harvest (see Table 6-9 for example). Later, as the pool mills and sells some or all of the rice in the pool at what it believes is to the best advantage, further advances will be made to the growers involved. The amounts depend upon how well the pool performs and will almost certainly total the support price less storage costs and very likely will total more.

FUTURE ADJUSTMENTS

Indications are that the current trends to increased acreage allotments and production per acre will continue, thus necessitating additional facilities for rough rice drying and storage. Assuming that some 16 million more hundredweight will be produced annually in the United States by 1975 than in 1967, about $20 million in additional investments in capacity will be needed to handle the average crop at that time. Louisiana and Texas would each need about $5 million in such additional facilities if they share this increase in proportion to what they now produce under the present system; with widespread adoption of commingling little new investment would be needed!

Since commingling is already extensively practiced in Arkansas and California, the industry in these two states is faced with little choice other than to expand or not have facilities available should the increased production trends be realized.

Facilities

In order to dry and store the crop in years of peak production the industry must provide facilities that will be under-utilized in other years. In future years when conservation of government funds is being emphasized, the size of the crop could be considerably less; in other years when policies such as "food for peace," agribusiness employment, or a favorable balance of payments are being emphasized, the crop may be even larger than projected.

141

TABLE 6-8. CONVERSION FACTORS FOR ESTIMATING ROUGH RICE YIELDS FROM VARYING LEVELS OF MOISTURE CONTENT

A	B	A	B	A	B	A	B
13.0	100.00	17.0	95.40	21.0	90.80	25.0	86.21
1	99.89	1	95.29	1	90.69	1	86.09
2	99.77	2	95.17	2	90.57	2	85.98
3	99.65	3	95.06	3	90.46	3	85.86
4	99.54	4	94.94	4	90.34	4	85.75
5	99.43	5	94.83	5	90.23	5	85.63
6	99.31	6	94.71	6	90.12	6	85.52
7	99.20	7	94.60	7	90.00	7	85.40
8	99.08	8	94.48	8	89.89	8	85.29
9	98.97	9	94.37	9	89.77	9	85.17
14.0	98.85	18.0	94.25	22.0	89.66	26.0	85.06
1	98.74	1	94.14	1	89.54	1	84.94
2	98.62	2	94.02	2	89.43	2	84.83
3	98.51	3	93.91	3	89.31	3	84.71
4	98.39	4	93.79	4	89.20	4	84.60
5	98.28	5	93.68	5	89.08	5	84.48
6	98.16	6	93.56	6	88.97	6	84.37
7	98.05	7	93.45	7	88.85	7	84.25
8	97.93	8	93.33	8	88.74	8	84.14
9	97.82	9	93.22	9	88.62	9	84.02
15.0	97.70	19.0	93.10	23.0	88.51	27.0	83.91
1	97.59	1	92.99	1	88.39	1	83.79
2	97.47	2	92.87	2	88.28	2	83.68
3	97.36	3	92.76	3	88.16	3	83.56
4	97.24	4	92.64	4	88.05	4	83.45
5	97.13	5	92.53	5	87.93	5	83.33
6	97.01	6	92.41	6	87.82	6	83.22
7	96.90	7	92.30	7	87.70	7	83.10
8	96.78	8	92.18	8	87.59	8	82.99
9	96.67	9	92.07	9	87.47	9	82.87
16.0	96.55	20.0	91.95	24.0	87.36	28.0	82.76
1	96.44	1	91.84	1	87.24	1	82.64
2	96.32	2	91.72	2	87.13	2	82.53
3	96.21	3	91.61	3	87.01	3	82.41
4	96.09	4	91.49	4	86.90	4	82.30
5	95.98	5	91.38	5	86.78	5	82.19
6	95.86	6	91.26	6	86.67	6	82.07
7	95.75	7	91.15	7	86.55	7	81.95
8	95.63	8	91.03	8	86.44	8	81.84
9	95.52	9	90.92	9	86.32	9	81.72
13.0	100.00	17.0	95.40	21.0	90.80	25.0	86.21
1	99.89	1	95.29	1	90.69	1	86.09
2	99.77	2	95.17	2	90.57	2	85.98
3	99.65	3	95.06	3	90.46	3	85.86
4	99.54	4	94.94	4	90.34	4	85.75
5	99.43	5	94.83	5	90.23	5	85.63
6	99.31	6	94.71	6	90.12	6	85.52
7	99.20	7	94.60	7	90.00	7	85.40
8	99.08	8	94.48	8	89.89	8	85.29
9	98.97	9	94.37	9	89.77	9	85.17

TABLE 6-8. (Continued)

A	B	A	B	A	B	A	B
14.0	98.85	18.0	94.25	22.0	89.66	26.0	85.06
1	98.74	1	94.14	1	89.54	1	84.94
2	98.62	2	94.02	2	89.43	2	84.83
3	98.51	3	93.91	3	89.31	3	84.71
4	98.39	4	93.79	4	89.20	4	84.60
5	98.28	5	93.68	5	89.08	5	84.48
6	98.16	6	93.56	6	88.97	6	84.37
7	98.05	7	93.45	7	88.85	7	84.25
8	97.93	8	93.33	8	88.74	8	84.14
9	97.82	9	93.22	9	88.62	9	84.02
15.0	97.70	19.0	93.10	23.0	88.51	27.0	83.91
1	97.59	1	92.99	1	88.39	1	83.79
2	97.47	2	92.87	2	88.28	2	83.68
3	97.36	3	92.76	3	88.16	3	83.56
4	97.24	4	92.64	4	88.05	4	83.45
5	97.13	5	92.53	5	87.93	5	83.33
6	97.01	6	92.41	6	87.82	6	83.22
7	96.90	7	92.30	7	87.70	7	83.10
8	96.78	8	92.18	8	87.59	8	82.99
9	96.67	9	92.07	9	87.47	9	82.87
16.0	96.55	20.0	91.95	24.0	87.36	28.0	82.76
1	96.44	1	91.84	1	87.24	1	82.64
2	96.32	2	91.72	2	87.13	2	82.53
3	96.21	3	91.61	3	87.01	3	82.41
4	96.09	4	91.49	4	86.90	4	82.30
5	95.98	5	91.38	5	86.78	5	82.19
6	95.86	6	91.26	6	86.67	6	82.07
7	95.75	7	91.15	7	86.55	7	81.95
8	95.63	8	91.03	8	86.44	8	81.84
9	95.52	9	90.92	9	86.32	9	81.72

Column A—percent of moisture content.
Column B—percent of rough rice yield.

This is not a new phenomenon and is not unique to rice. Since domestic production of rice is a relatively small proportion of world production it is perhaps more vulnerable in this respect than other major crops, however. During the early part of the last decade, for example, government programs allowed a tremendous increase in annual production of and in government owned stocks of rice (Table 6-10). Those with access to available drying and storage facilities made large profits. Resort was made to storage in sacks, railroad cars and other expedients. Later, acreage was reduced by about 40 percent over a 2-year period and the demand for facilities was reduced further by other government programs designed to reduce government owned stocks of rice. Many of these facilities operated at a loss for a time and then ceased operations. Others operated at less than capacity, some of them obviously operating at a loss on an annual basis.

TABLE 6-9. SCHEDULE OF ADVANCES FOR BLUEBONNET RICE, 1966-67 SEASON

Fancy produced	Government support price	Grades 1 to 5 (78%) 1-2 Plus 5¢ 3 Base price 4 Minus 5¢ 5 Minus 15¢	Grade 6 (62%)	Sample (49%) 7-8-9	Grades (39%) 10-11-12
			— — Dollars per bushel — — — — — —		
114 pounds total clean					
95-100	2.40	1.90	1.50	1.20	.95
90-95	2.33	1.85	1.45	1.15	.90
85-90	2.27	1.80	1.40	1.10	.90
80-85	2.21	1.75	1.35	1.05	.85
75-80	2.15	1.70	1.30	1.05	.85
70-75	2.08	1.65	1.30	1.00	.80
65-70	2.02	1.60	1.25	1.00	.80
60-65	1.96	1.55	1.20	.95	.75
55-60	1.89	1.50	1.15	.95	.75
50-55	1.82	1.45	1.15	.90	.70
45-50	1.77	1.40	1.10	.85	.70
40-45	1.70	1.35	1.05	.85	.65
112 pounds total clean					
95-100	2.38	1.85	1.45	1.15	.90
90-95	2.31	1.80	1.40	1.15	.90
85-90	2.25	1.75	1.40	1.10	.85
80-85	2.19	1.70	1.35	1.05	.85
75-80	2.12	1.65	1.30	1.05	.85
70-75	2.06	1.60	1.30	1.00	.80
65-70	2.00	1.55	1.25	1.00	.80
60-65	1.94	1.50	1.20	.95	.75
55-60	1.87	1.45	1.15	.90	.75
50-55	1.81	1.40	1.10	.90	.70
45-50	1.75	1.35	1.10	.85	.70
40-45	1.68	1.30	1.05	.80	.65
110 pounds total clean					
95-100	2.35	1.85	1.45	1.15	.90
90-95	2.29	1.80	1.40	1.10	.90
85-90	2.23	1.75	1.40	1.10	.85
80-85	2.17	1.70	1.35	1.05	.85
75-80	2.10	1.65	1.30	1.00	.80
70-75	2.04	1.60	1.25	1.00	.80
65-70	1.98	1.55	1.20	.95	.75
60-65	1.91	1.50	1.20	.95	.75
55-60	1.85	1.45	1.15	.90	.70
50-55	1.79	1.40	1.10	.90	.70
45-50	1.73	1.35	1.05	.85	.65
40-45	1.66	1.30	1.05	.80	.65

TABLE 6-10. ROUGH RICE SUPPLY AND DISTRIBUTION, U.S., 1951-67

Crop year[1]	Carryover	Production	Distribution
	— — — — — — 1,000 cwt. — — — — — —		
1951	2,300	46,089	46,672
1952	781	48,193	48,485
1953	776	52,834	50,803
1954	3,427	64,193	56,866
1955	8,736	55,902	47,147
1956	18,294	47,402	53,928
1957	13,952	41,877	45,961
1958	10,527	47,015	46,255
1959	7,069	53,647	52,903
1960	7,813	54,591	55,063
1961	7,341	54,198	58,399
1962	3,140	66,045	63,531
1963	5,654	70,083	70,548
1964	5,189	72,483	73,448
1965	4,905	76,281	75,706
1966	5,480	85,060	84,350
1967	6,190	90,614	

[1]Year begins August 1 for Southern area and U.S. and October for California.
Source: *Rice, Annual Market Summary*, Grain Division, AMS, USDA, various issues.

Of the 235 known on-farm facilites in operation in Louisiana and Texas in 1959, 133, or more than half, were built during the 4 years, 1953, 1954, 1955 and 1956 (Table 6-11). Considering the large annual carryovers of rice prior to and during the early part of this period, available facilities were very limited. As more capacity was constructed and as the annual carryover was reduced producers marketing opportunities were somewhat enhanced. By 1957 new construction of farm facilities had dropped considerably as the returns from storage became less lucrative (Figure 6-3).

Under such circumstances, the costs for drying and storage are greater than if more stable demand could be counted on. A conscious government policy of maintaining larger average annual carryovers of rice from year to year could reduce the need for such erratic production and its ancillary erratic demand for drying and storage facilities. This would probably require additional federal legislation. However, a more stable and efficient industry in the years to come would result.

Commingling

Outright purchases and sales by driers and mills, seasonal pools, and other methods could be used to consumate commingling. These approaches, however, mean that operators would need a great deal more working capital than they now use. Commercial credit is

145

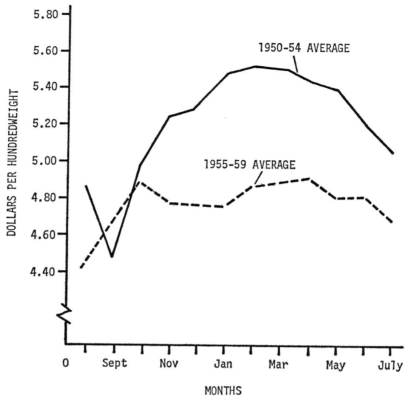

Figure 6-3. Simple Monthly Average Prices received for Rough Rice by Louisiana Farmers, 1950-54 and 1955-59.

Source: Crop Reporting Board, AMS, USDA, Washington, D.C.

normally available for a large part of such needs. The working capital would be needed to purchase green rice or to make advances to those who choose seasonal pools.

Marketing organizations separate from mills or driers might handle the purchases and sales of rice and/or utilize seasonal pools. This would allow drying and storage facilities to continue operating on a custom basis but rather than having to preserve lots on an ownership identity basis, it could be commingled.

For farmer cooperatives, borrowing under the government price support loan program may also be feasible except for loans to mill facilities on their own warehouse receipts. Farmer cooperatives may borrow against the support price for rice in much the same manner as an individual farmer. The current interest rate under this program

TABLE 6-11. NUMBER OF FARM DRYERS, AGGREGATE STORAGE CAPACITY AND YEAR OF CONSTRUCTION, LOUISIANA AND TEXAS, 1948-58

Year	Louisiana		Texas	
	Number	Storage capacity	Number	Storage capacity
		1,000 cwt.		1,000 cwt.
1948	7	171.7	2	91.2
1949	5	55.9		
1950	2	12.2		
1951	3	18.1	3	37.6
1952	9	80.5	2	43.7
1953	14	116.2	7	58.6
1954	29	198.3	12	124.3
1955	21	178.2	21	245.6
1956	12	71.6	17	193.9
1957	7	33.9	12	121.2
1958	6	34.3	10	107.6
Unknown[1]	5	Unknown	29	Unknown
Total	120	970.9	115	1,023.7

[1]Several owners of farm drying and storage units were either not sure of details or unwilling to provide information.

is about 3.5 percent, a very decided advantage in these times when commercial interest rates are relatively high.

It should be noted that if the industry moves in the direction of commingling, seasonal pools, selling agents and cooperatives, the burden of speculation, of necessity long carried in large part by mills in Louisiana and Texas, will tend to be shifted away from them toward producers. A farmer cooperative, for example, pays all its expenses, sets aside reserves for depreciation, and such before distributing available funds to farmers based on the volume of rice handled for each producer. If such funds are large, the dividends likely will be generous; if small or if conditions have been unfavorable in previous years there may be none. Independent operators, on the other hand, obtain large earnings in certain years and perhaps operate at a loss during others.

Pools can also be and are operated by other than cooperatives. Numerous possibilities for such arrangements exist making it impossible to list, much less evaluate alternatives facing the industry.

Consolidations of varying degrees are taking place in the rice industry. These range from simple horizontal integration of farmers, millers and other segments of the industry to forward integration by farmers and backyard integration by millers. Some of these no doubt result in technical efficiencies such as large scale production, more even flow of business and elimination of wasteful competition while others result in a potential lessening of competition.

Farmers over the nation and locally are conscious of better organization as a method of gaining a "fair share" through bargaining. This idea is also being aggressively encouraged by top U. S. Department of Agriculture officials. Further development of commingling, seasonal pools, bargaining associations, selling agents, marketing orders, marketing agreements, cooperatives and combinations of these will likely be hastened by these attitudes.

If rice producers choose to move more in the direction of cooperatives, decisions will have to be made as to whether more facilities should be operated at all by them and if so, should they be owned, leased or perhaps subcontracted. If they move in other directions such as marketing orders or selling agents, the relevant decisions to be made will be different and the structure of the drying and storage industry will be affected accordingly.

7

Rice Transportation Rates and Systems

Gene F. Miller

A comparison of transportation rates and services among the several rice producing areas is used as a basis for recommending changes in transporting rice in the Gulf area.

Regardless of where rice may be produced, transportation rates and services are important in determining how, when and where the national rice supply is marketed. Further, the competitive level of freight rates among different transportation modes usually determines the kind of carrier that hauls the traffic.

Much of the data shown on transportation rates and services are based on information obtained by personal interview from officials of rice marketing and processing cooperatives in Arkansas, Texas, Louisiana and California. Supplemental information was obtained from secondary sources including published reports of the Interstate Commerce Commission and the U. S. Department of Agriculture.

COMPARATIVE FREIGHT RATES AND CHARGES

Comparative rail freight rates on rice from representative drying points through milling points to principal markets follow. Rates shown are the sum of rates on dried rough rice from drying point to mill and for milled rice from mill to market. Truck rates are typical of those quoted by truckers hauling rice between the points shown.

Water rates shown are for export only. None of the firms interviewed shipped rice over the inland, coastal or intercoastal waterways during 1966.

Rail Rates

Table 7-1 shows rates from selected origins in Arkansas, Louisiana, Texas and California to principal consuming markets in the United States. Each rate shown is the sum of a rate on dried rough rice from detached drier to mill and a rate on milled rice from mill to principal consuming markets. For each origin and destination, the analysis uses the lowest carload rates available, and reflects transit privileges and charges where applicable.

149

TABLE 7-1. RAIL FREIGHT RATES ON RICE PER 100 POUNDS[1] FROM SELECTED SOUTHERN DRYING AND MILLING POINTS TO PRINCIPAL MARKETS OUTSIDE THE SOUTHERN RICE STATES, JULY 1, 1967

		Northern markets									
		Chicago, Ill.		Milwaukee, Wis.		Detroit, Mich.		Cleveland, Ohio		New York, N.Y.	
Drying point	Milling point	40,000 pounds[2]	Excess[2]	40,000 pounds	Excess	40,000 pounds	Excess	40,000 pounds	Excess	40,000 pounds	Excess
						Cents					
Arkansas[3]	Arkansas[3]										
Parkin	Jonesboro	61.0	50.0	69.0	57.0	83.5	68.0	85.5	69.0	121.5	98.5
Weiner	Jonesboro	59.0	48.0	67.0	55.0	81.5	66.0	83.5	67.0	119.5	96.5
North Little Rock	Stuttgart	59.0	48.0	67.0	55.0	81.5	66.0	83.5	67.0	119.5	96.5
McGehee	Stuttgart	61.0	50.0	69.0	57.0	83.5	68.0	85.5	69.0	121.5	98.5
Wheatley	Stuttgart	59.0	48.0	67.0	55.0	81.5	66.0	83.5	67.0	119.5	96.5
Louisiana											
Oberlin	Crowley	77.5	62.0	83.5	67.0	100.5	81.5	102.5	82.5	138.5	111.5
Eunice	Crowley	77.5	62.0	83.5	67.0	100.5	81.5	102.5	82.5	138.5	111.5
Mermentau	Crowley	77.5	62.0	83.5	67.0	100.5	81.5	102.5	82.5	138.5	111.5
Texas											
Katy	Houston	81.5	66.0	87.5	70.5	102.5	82.5	104.5	84.5	140.5	113.5
Eagle Lake	Houston	81.5	66.0	87.5	70.5	102.5	82.5	104.5	84.5	140.5	113.5
Dayton	Houston	81.5	66.0	87.5	70.5	102.5	82.5	104.5	84.5	140.5	113.5

TABLE 7-1. (Continued)

Drying point	Milling point	Charleston, S.C. 40,000 Pounds²	Excess²	Southeastern markets Savannah, Ga. 40,000 pounds	Excess	Miami, Fla. 40,000 pounds	Excess	Western markets San Francisco, Calif. 100,000 pounds	Excess
					— Cents —				
Arkansas³	Arkansas³								
Parkin	Jonesboro	76.5	62.0	73.5	60.0	93.5	76.5	88.5	72.0
Weiner	Jonesboro	74.5	60.0	71.5	58.0	91.5	74.5	86.5	70.0
North Little Rock	Stuttgart	74.5	60.0	71.5	58.0	91.5	74.5	86.5	70.0
McGehee	Stuttgart	76.5	62.0	73.5	60.0	93.5	76.5	88.5	72.0
Wheatley	Stuttgart	74.5	60.0	71.5	58.0	91.5	74.5	86.5	70.0
Louisiana									
Oberlin	Crowley	77.5	62.0	73.5	59.0	88.5	71.5	85.5	69.0
Eunice	Crowley	77.5	62.0	73.5	59.0	88.5	71.5	85.5	69.0
Mermentau	Crowley	77.5	62.0	73.5	59.0	88.5	71.5	85.5	69.0
Texas									
Katy	Houston	88.5	72.0	82.5	66.5	100.5	82.5	85.5	69.0
Eagle Lake	Houston	88.5	72.0	82.5	66.5	100.5	82.5	77.5	69.0
Dayton	Houston	83.5	67.0	77.5	61.5	95.5	77.5	77.5	69.0

¹Each rate shown is the sum of a rate on dried rough rice from drying point to milling point plus the rate on milled rice to consuming markets. They are the lowest carload rates available and reflect transit privileges and charges where applicable.

²Rates in the first column under each market apply on each 100 pounds up to the weight shown. Rates in the second column marked "Excess" apply on each 100 pounds over the weight shown.

³Among the rates on rice originated at drying points in Arkansas and milled in Arkansas mills are differences according to whether the movement is a singleline or jointline haul. For a singleline haul (one with both the drying and the milling point on the same railroad), the net local rate after deducting the cutback is 4.5 cents per 100 pounds for hauls of 135 miles or less. For a jointline haul (one with drying and the milling point on different railroads), the net local rate on such movements is two cents per 100 pounds higher.

151

TABLE 7-1. (Continued)

		Northern markets							
		Chicago, Ill.		Milwaukee, Wis.		Detroit, Mich.		Cleveland, Ohio	
Drying point	Milling point	100,000# minimum in boxcars	142,000# minimum in hoppers	100,000# minimum in boxcars	142,000# minimum in hoppers	100,000# minimum in boxcars	142,000# minimum in hoppers	100,000# minimum in boxcars	142,000# minimum in hoppers
		— — — — — — — — Cents — — — — — — —							
Biggs	W. Sacramento	121.5	108.5	121.5	108.5	121.5	115.5	126.5	120.5
Mendota	W. Sacramento	115.5	102.5	115.5	102.5	115.5	109.5	120.5	114.5
Woodland	W. Sacramento	116.5	103.5	116.5	103.5	116.5	110.5	121.5	115.5

		Northern markets	Southeastern markets		
		New York, N.Y.	Charleston, S.C.	Savannah, Ga.	Miami, Fla.
Biggs	W. Sacramento	158.5 150.5	152.4 147.4	146.0 141.0	162.8 157.8
Mendota	W. Sacramento	152.5 144.5	146.4 141.4	140.0 135.0	156.8 151.8
Woodland	W. Sacramento	153.5 145.5	147.4 142.4	141.0 136.0	157.8 152.8

¹Each rate shown is the sum of a rate on dried rough rice from drying point to milling point plus the rate on milled rice to consuming markets. They are the lowest carload rates available and reflect transit privileges and charges where applicable.

Arkansas has a rail rate advantage over Louisiana and Texas to northern markets. Louisiana and Arkansas rail rates are lower than those from Texas to Savannah, Georgia, and other major southeastern markets. Rail rates from California are much higher than from Louisiana, Arkansas and Texas to northern and southeastern markets.

California rate levels are generally based on varying minimum weights and whether boxcars or covered hopper cars are used.

Truck Rates

Table 7-2 presents truck rates (as well as comparable rail rates) from selected origins in the Southern rice area and California to principal markets in the United States. Truck freight rates are higher than rail rates between all points shown. Each truck rate is the sum of a rate on dried rough rice from driers to mill and a rate on milled rice from mill to principal consuming markets. For each origin and destination, the analysis uses the lowest truck rate available. Rates were obtained from the firms interviewed and were stated to be typical rates quoted by motor carriers hauling a significant volume of rice by truck between specified origins and destinations.

At least three important structural differences exist between truck and rail rates on rice. First, truck rates do not provide for transit privileges. Second, rail carload minimums are generally between 40 and 70 tons, while truck minimums are usually lower—typically 15 or 20 tons. Third, truck rates on rice generally vary according to mileage involved, while rates for rail carriers diminish on a per-ton basis with longer hauls. Because rice is an exempt agricultural commodity under Interstate Commerce Commission regulations, interstate truck rates are generally determined by availability of trucks and negotiations between shipper and trucker. In contrast, rail rates are established by the Interstate Commerce Commission.

Generally, the disparity between truck and rail rates increases with length of haul. For example, on rice dried at McGehee, Arkansas, and milled at Stuttgart, Arkansas, the rail rate to Chicago, Illinois, is 21.6 cents per hundredweight below the truck rate (a total rail mileage distance of about 700 miles), Table 7-2. From the same origin points to New York City, a distance of about 1,600 miles, the rail rate is 27.3 cents lower than the truck rate. Rate comparisons from the above origins to San Francisco, California, a 2,600-mile haul, show a difference of 46.5 cents.

Water — Export Rates

Water shipments other than to export markets are insignificant for all mills. Export shipments, however, are extremely important to all rice producing regions as exports in recent years have dominated

TABLE 7-2. COMPARISON BETWEEN RAIL[1] AND MOTORTRUCK RATES ON RICE, PER 100 POUNDS, FROM SELECTED SOUTHERN AND CALIFORNIA DRYING AND MILLING POINTS TO PRINCIPAL MARKETS IN THE U.S., JULY 1, 1967[2]

Northern markets

Drying point	Milling point	Chicago, Ill.			Milwaukee, Wis.			Detroit, Mich.		
		Mileage[3]	Rail rates	Truck rates	Mileage[3]	Rail rates	Truck rates	Mileage[3]	Rail rates	Truck rates
		Miles	Cents	Cents	Miles	Cents	Cents	Miles	Cents	Cents
McGehee, Ark.	Stuttgart, Ark.	727	54.4	76.0	822	61.8	92.0	973	74.2	103.0
Mermentau, La.	Crowley, La.	1,092	68.2	75.0	1,188	73.6	90.0	1,343	89.1	100.0
Dayton, Tex.	Houston, Tex.	1,220	72.2	74.0	1,314	77.3	86.0	1,459	90.5	95.0
Biggs, Calif.	Sacramento, Calif.	2,461	121.5	192.0	2,511	121.5	192.0	2,763	121.5	207.0

Northern markets / Western markets

Drying point	Milling point	Cleveland, Ohio			New York, N. Y.			San Francisco, Calif.		
		Mileage[3]	Rail rates	Truck rates	Mileage[3]	Rail rates	Truck rates	Mileage[3]	Rail rates	Truck rates
		Miles	Cents	Cents	Miles	Cents	Cents	Miles	Cents	Cents
McGehee, Ark.	Stuttgart, Ark.	1,029	75.6	103.0	1,614	107.7	135.0	2,620	88.5	135.0
Mermentau, La.	Crowley, La.	1,399	90.5	100.0	1,984	122.3	140.0	2,565	85.5	130.0
Dayton, Tex.	Houston, Tex.	1,515	92.5	94.0	2,100	124.3	134.0	2,345	77.5	129.0
Biggs, Calif.	Sacramento, Calif.	2,836	126.5	242.0	3,467	158.5	257.0	155	35.5	43.0

Southeastern markets

Drying point	Milling point	Charleston, S. C.			Savannah, Ga.			Miami, Fla.		
		Mileage[3]	Rail rates	Truck rates	Mileage[3]	Rail rates	Truck rates	Mileage[3]	Rail rates	Truck rates
		Miles	Cents	Cents	Miles	Cents	Cents	Miles	Cents	Cents
McGehee, Ark.	Stuttgart, Ark.	987	67.8	92.0	923	65.4	85.0	1,309	83.3	103.0
Mermentau, La.	Crowley, La.	1,089	68.2	90.0	984	64.8	87.0	1,279	78.3	100.0
Dayton, Tex.	Houston, Tex.	1,292	73.6	94.0	1,187	67.9	89.0	1,482	84.7	89.0
Biggs, Calif.	Sacramento, Calif.	3,517	152.4	207.0	3,412	146.0	207.0	3,707	162.8	217.0

[1]Rail rates are based on carload movements of 100,000 pounds per carload.

[2]Each rate shown is the sum of a rate on dried rough rice from drying point to milling point plus the rate on milled rice to consuming markets. They are the lowest carload rates available and reflect transit privileges and charges where applicable.

[3]Mileage figures are based on railroad miles from drying points to market (combination of short line plus 28300 mileage scale plus 13 percent circuity factor),

Note: Railroad rates are from published tariffs. Truck rates are from tariffs on file with the state regulatory commissions and the Interstate Commerce Commission are from rates quoted by "for-hire carriers" to the firms interviewed. Rail rates reflect transit privileges and charges where applicable.

154

U. S. milled rice disappearance, accounting for around 60 percent of total U. S. production. Table 7-3, shows export movements of rice from the South and from California by major ports in the continental United States for 1951-64.

Freight rates for rice moving into export channels may be either published or negotiated. So-called published rates are generally higher than negotiated rates and most rice moves on rates negotiated between shippers and ocean carriers. General information regarding application of rail rates for rice when moving to port is illustrated in footnote 1.[1]

Table 7-4 gives examples of negotiated export rates on rice from Gulf and California ports to selected foreign markets in 1967.

Export rates from Sacramento to Japan and Vietnam are lower than from Gulf ports. Rates from the Gulf ports and Sacramento to Germany are about the same. The rates in the tabulation do not include loading, unloading or other port charges. These vary substantially between ports and often are the deciding factor in determining the specific port at which shipments may be loaded, especially within a shipping region. Loading or stevedoring charges are about $8 per long ton higher at West Coast ports than at Gulf ports. Port charges at Gulf ports are about $4 per long ton and are about $12 per long ton at West Coast ports. Table 7-5 illustrates total charges for milled rice in bags for export from various Louisiana shipping point origins to selected port destinations in this state. Table 7-6 compares wharfage and unloading charges on milled rice at various Gulf ports.

COMPARATIVE TON-MILE RAIL RATES

Rail charges per ton-mile typically bear an inverse relationship to distance. That is, as distance increases, ton-mile costs decrease. For example, on rice dried at McGehee, Arkansas, and milled at Stuttgart, Arkansas, the per-ton-mile rate to Chicago, Illinois (about 700 miles) is 1½ cents, Table 7-7. From the same origins to San Francisco,

---

[1] Item 2400-C, Southwestern Lines Freight Tariff 282-C, publishes export rates as shown in (a) and (b) below on milled rice, in bags, from all Arkansas rice mill origins to all Gulf Ports, Pensacola, Fla., to, but not including, Corpus Christi, Texas. *Rates apply only on a non-shipside basis.* Rates *do not* include the cost of handling, loading, unloading, wharfage/tollage, nor other terminal charges at the ports, except will include switching charges to the extent the absorption is authorized in tariffs on file with the Interstate Commerce Commission. All charges not absorbed are in addition to the rail rates.

(a) Single car rate is 27½ cents per 100 pounds, minimum weight 100,000 pounds.

(b) Multiple car rate is 25 cents per 100 pounds, minimum weight 120,000 pounds per car, subject to an aggregate minimum weight of 600 short tons per shipment under one bill of loading, from one consignor at one milling point, to one consignee at one time, to one port of exit.

TABLE 7-3. EXPORT MOVEMENTS OF RICE FROM THE SOUTH AND FROM CALIFORNIA BY MAJOR PORT IN CONTINENTAL U.S., 1951-64

Port	Exports						
	1951	1952	1953	1954	1955	1956	1957
	Tons						
Gulf ports							
Lake Charles, La.	179,849	268,036	243,297	196,764	140,150	302,796	210,224
Houston, Tex.	129,533	208,781	156,403	147,264	127,453	290,867	235,030
New Orleans, La.	61,758	80,589	44,572	58,279	67,312	109,394	102,700
Beaumont, Tex.	21,647	27,071	28,939	22,961	23,334	63,425	18,830
Orange, Tex.	251	8,622	7,414	6,244	7,072	23,931	6,172
Galveston, Tex.	1,777	3,378	422	610	246	59,806	35,129
Texas City, Tex.							
West Coast ports							
Stockton, Calif.	29,382	76,644	62,501	101,217	106,793	14,225	123,998
San Francisco, Calif.	26,063	66,691	51,752	58,689	83,278	8,052	31,264
Oakland, Calif.	14,904	12,080	27,984	1,226	670	1,227	956
Atlantic ports							
New York Port	1,953	1,647	1,915	119	271	536	704
Philadelphia Harbor	178	66	1	79	3	770	69
Jacksonville, Fla.	6	159	99	77	150	136	222
Boston, Mass.	1					8	10

TABLE 7-3. (Continued)

	Exports						
Port	1958	1959	1960	1961	1962	1963	1964
	— — — — — — — Tons — — — — — — —						
Gulf ports							
Lake Charles, La.	255,891	263,323	371,018	323,933	539,284	497,986	577,503
Houston, Tex.	240,107	269,369	383,563	280,844	295,938	326,720	381,366
New Orleans, La.	45,449	28,577	123,100	72,626	75,657	125,017	123,672
Beaumont, Tex.	13,233	24,322	45,112	42,595	32,957	21,506	26,662
Orange, Tex.	2,687	6,870	26,985	12,874	41,117	50,085	48,001
Galveston, Tex.	5,745	6,732	4,056	352	25	3,208	23,725
Texas City, Tex.	38,645						120
West Coast ports							
Stockton, Calif.	37,562	135,584	90,529	117,091	147,784	202,818	49,104
San Francisco, Calif.	11,944	12,237	21,494	32,391	23,546	37,167	27,157
Oakland, Calif.	8,291	10,911	3,610	1,889		4,150	1,398
Atlantic ports							
New York Port	506	518	543	597	579	957	607
Philadelphia Harbor	67	122	159	38	62	15	10
Jacksonville, Fla.	340	2,162	2,230	1,831	2,121	2,054	2,703
Boston, Mass.					12		

Source: Department of the Army, Corps of Engineers, *Waterborne Commerce of the United States.*

157

TABLE 7-4. NEGOTIATED EXPORT RATES ON RICE FROM GULF AND CALIFORNIA PORTS TO SELECTED FOREIGN MARKETS, 1967

Origin	Destination		
	Japan bulk	Vietnam 100 pound bags	Germany bulk
	— — — — Cents per 2,000 pounds — — — —		
Gulf ports	13.50	25.40	7.00
Sacramento, Calif.	9.00	22.25	7.10

TABLE 7-5. MILLED RICE, IN BAGS FOR EXPORT FROM LOUISIANA ORIGINS TO LAKE CHARLES, BATON ROUGE AND NEW ORLEANS, LOUISIANA, IN CENTS PER 2,000 POUNDS, 1967

Origin	To Lake Charles present charges	To Baton Rouge present charges	To New Orleans present charges
	— — — — Cents per 2,000 pounds — — — —		
Abbeville			
Rail rate	210	430	350
Unloading	162	128	145
Wharfage	35	35	35
Total shipside	407	593	530
Crowley			
Rail rate	210	290	350
Unloading	162	128	145
Wharfage	35	35	35
Total shipside	407	453	530
Eunice			
Rail rate	210	250	350
Unloading	162	128	145
Wharfage	35	35	35
Total shipside	407	413	530

California (about 2,600 miles) it is approximately 1 cent. All other points listed in the table exhibit similar characteristics.

The per-ton-mile rate from California is lower to *all* the markets analyzed than are the respective rates from the Southern rice area. The ton-mile rate from Texas is lower than the rate from Louisiana which is in turn lower than the Arkansas rate.

Comparison of Carrier Revenue to Transportation Costs

Two measures are available for examining the extent to which hauling rice is a profitable or unprofitable venture for rail carriers. These measures consist of the relationship of (1) out-of-pocket and

TABLE 7-6. COMPARISON OF WHARFAGE/UNLOADING CHARGES ON MILLED RICE AT GULF PORTS IN CENTS PER 2,000 POUNDS, 1967

| Port | Charges | | |
	Wharfage	Unloading	Total
	— — — — Cents per 2,000 pounds — — — —		
Gulfport	28	85	113
Mobile	28	85	113
Pascagoula	28	85	113
Pensacola	28	85	113
Orange	15	132	147
Baton Rouge	35	128	163
New Orleans			
Stuyvesant Docks		145	145
Public Wharves[1]	35	145	180
Beaumont	15[2]	172	187
Lake Charles	35	162	197
Port Arthur	35	205	240
Galveston	35	215	250
Houston	35	215	250
Freeport	35	215	250
Texas City	35	215	250

[1]Plus $4.95 per car unabsorbed switching charge—Public Belt Railroad.

[2]15 cents wharfage charge at Beaumont applies only on rice from Arkansas origins. From Louisiana and Texas origins the wharfage charge is 35 cents.

(2) fully distributed costs to the rates which rail carriers charge for their services.[2]

Table 7-8 compares rail revenues (rates) to out-of-pocket and fully distributed costs from selected drying and milling points in the South and California to principal markets in the United States.

The information shown in Table 7-8 illustrates that heavier carloadings result in reductions in both revenues and costs, with the

[2]The comparisons that follow are more impressive when the ICC Bureau's definitions of out-of-pocket and fully distributed costs are considered. Out-of-pocket costs are defined as "those expenses which, over the long term period, are variable with the volume of traffic handled." They include 80 percent of the operating expenses, plus an allowance for return at 4 percent on 50 percent of the real property and 100 percent of the equipment.

Fully distributed costs are the sum of out-of-pocket costs (as thus defined) and the "apportioned overhead burden." The latter term includes "the remaining operating expenses, rents, and taxes, and allowance for return not included in the out-of-pocket costs, the sum of which was distributed among the commodities on a ton and ton-mile basis. In addition, the total overhead burden thus indicated also included any deficits incurred in the passenger-train and less-carload services, and the allowance for return was adjusted to reflect the actual rate of return earned by the carriers in 1965."

Source: Interstate Commerce Commission, Bureau of Accounts and Cost Finding, *Rail Carload Unit Costs by Territories for the Year 1965.* Statement No. 7-67.

TABLE 7-7. COMPARISON OF RAIL CARLOAD, PER-TON AND PER-TON MILE COST ON RICE, FROM SELECTED SOUTHERN AND CALIFORNIA DRYING AND MILLING POINTS TO PRINCIPAL MARKETS IN THE U.S., JULY 1, 1967

Northern markets

Drying point	Milling point	Chicago, Illinois Mileage	50-ton carload cost	Cost per ton	Per-ton mile cost	Milwaukee, Wisconsin Mileage	50-ton carload cost	Cost per ton	Per-ton mile cost
		Miles	— Dollars —	— Dollars —	Cents	Miles	— Dollars —	— Dollars —	Cents
McGehee, Ark.	Stuttgart, Ark.	727	544	10.88	1.50	822	618	12.36	1.50
Mermentau, La.	Crowley, La.	1,092	682	13.64	1.25	1,188	736	14.72	1.24
Dayton, Tex.	Houston, Tex.	1,220	722	14.44	1.18	1,314	733	15.46	1.18
Biggs, Calif.	Sacramento, Calif.	2,461	1,215	24.30	0.99	2,511	1,215	24.30	0.97

Northern markets

Drying point	Milling point	Detroit, Michigan Mileage	50-ton carload cost	Cost per ton	Per-ton mile cost	Cleveland, Ohio Mileage	50-ton carload cost	Cost per ton	Per-ton mile cost
McGehee, Ark.	Stuttgart, Ark.	973	742	14.84	1.53	1,029	756	15.12	1.47
Mermentau, La.	Crowley, La.	1,343	891	17.82	1.33	1,399	905	18.10	1.29
Dayton, Tex.	Houston, Tex.	1,459	905	18.10	1.24	1,515	925	18.50	1.22
Biggs, Calif.	Sacramento, Calif.	2,763	1,215	24.30	0.88	2,836	1,265	25.30	0.89

Northern markets / **Western markets**

Drying point	Milling point	New York, N.Y. Mileage	50-ton carload cost	Cost per ton	Per-ton mile cost	San Francisco, Calif. Mileage	50-ton carload cost	Cost per ton	Per-ton mile cost
McGehee, Ark.	Stuttgart, Ark.	1,614	1,077	21.54	1.33	2,620	885	17.70	0.68
Mermentau, La.	Crowley, La.	1,984	1,223	24.46	1.23	2,565	855	17.10	0.67
Dayton, Tex.	Houston, Tex.	2,100	1,243	24.86	1.18	2,345	775	15.50	0.66
Biggs, Calif.	Sacramento, Calif.	3,467	1,585	31.70	0.91	155	355	7.10	4.58

TABLE 7-7. (Continued)

Drying point	Milling point	Mileage	50-ton carload cost	Cost per ton	Per-ton mile cost	Mileage	50-ton carload cost	Cost per ton	Per-ton mile cost
					Southeastern markets				
		Charleston, South Carolina				Savannah, Georgia			
McGehee, Ark.	Stuttgart, Ark.	987	678	13.56	1.37	923	654	13.08	1.42
Mermentau, La.	Crowley, La.	1,089	682	13.64	1.25	984	648	12.96	1.32
Dayton, Tex.	Houston, Tex.	1,292	736	14.72	1.14	1,187	679	13.58	1.14
Biggs, Calif.	Sacramento, Calif.	3,517	1,524	30.48	0.87	3,412	1,460	29.20	0.86
					Southeastern markets				
		Miami, Florida							
McGehee, Ark.	Stuttgart, Ark.	1,309	833	16.66	1.27				
Mermentau, La.	Crowley, La.	1,279	783	15.66	1.22				
Dayton, Tex.	Houston, Tex.	1,482	847	16.94	1.14				
Biggs, Calif.	Sacramento, Calif.	3,707	1,628	32.56	0.88				

TABLE 7-8. COMPARISON OF RAIL REVENUE TO OUT-OF-POCKET COST AND FULLY DISTRIBUTED COST ON RICE, PER 100 POUNDS, FROM SELECTED SOUTHERN AND CALIFORNIA DRYING AND MILLING POINTS TO PRINCIPAL MARKETS IN THE U.S.[1]

Drying point	Milling point	Chicago, Ill.			Northern markets Milwaukee, Wis.			Detroit, Mich.		
		Revenue	Out of pocket cost	Fully distributed cost	Revenue	Out of pocket cost	Fully distributed cost	Revenue	Out of pocket cost	Fully distributed cost
		Cents								
Stuttgart, Ark.										
McGehee, Ark.	Boxcar — 80,000#	55.5	37.2	51.7	63.0	39.8	55.5	75.8	46.0	63.1
	Hopper car — 100,000#	54.4	37.0	51.5	61.8	40.0	55.7	74.2	46.6	53.7
	Hopper car — 175,000#	52.5	24.4	38.7	59.8	26.5	42.1	71.5	30.7	47.8
Crowley, La.										
Mermentau, La.	Boxcar — 80,000#	69.8	47.3	66.5	75.3	49.9	70.3	91.0	56.2	78.1
	Hopper car — 100,000#	68.2	48.5	67.7	73.6	51.5	72.0	89.1	58.2	80.2
	Hopper car — 175,000#	65.5	32.4	51.5	70.8	34.5	54.9	85.8	38.9	60.8
Houston, Tex.										
Dayton, Tex.	Boxcar — 80,000#	73.8	50.8	71.6	79.0	53.4	75.4	92.5	59.4	82.7
	Hopper car — 100,000#	72.2	52.5	73.4	77.3	55.5	77.6	90.5	61.9	85.3
	Hopper car — 175,000#	69.5	35.2	56.0	74.4	37.3	59.3	87.1	41.5	64.8
Sacramento, Calif.										
Biggs, Calif.	Boxcar — 80,000#	121.5	88.5	128.4	121.5	93.4	135.4	121.5	97.5	140.7
	Hopper car — 100,000#		93.7	133.6		98.7	140.7		103.9	147.2
	Hopper car — 175,000#	108.5	64.0	103.9	108.5	67.8	109.8	115.5	71.0	114.3

TABLE 7-8. (Continued)

| | | Northern markets | | | | | | Southeastern markets | | |
| | | Cleveland, Ohio | | | New York, N.Y. | | | Charleston, S. C. | | |
Drying point	Milling point	Revenue	Out of pocket cost	Fully distributed cost	Revenue	Out of pocket cost	Fully distributed cost	Revenue	Out of pocket cost	Fully distributed cost
							Cents			
	Stuttgart, Ark.									
McGehee, Ark.	Boxcar — 80,000#	77.3	47.7	65.6	110.0	65.8	90.8	69.3	42.5	59.5
	Hopper car — 100,000#	75.6	48.5	66.3	107.7	68.7	93.6	67.8	42.3	59.2
	Hopper car — 175,000#	72.8	32.0	49.8	103.8	45.9	70.8	65.3	28.3	45.2
	Crowley, La.									
Mermentau, La.	Boxcar — 80,000#	92.5	57.9	80.6	125.0	76.0	105.8	69.8	45.3	63.6
	Hopper car — 100,000#	90.5	60.1	82.8	122.3	80.3	110.1	68.2	45.4	63.7
	Hopper car — 175,000#	87.1	40.2	62.8	117.7	54.1	83.8	65.5	30.5	48.6
	Houston, Tex.									
Dayton, Tex.	Boxcar — 80,000#	94.5	61.1	85.2	127.0	79.2	110.4	75.3	50.9	71.8
	Hopper car — 100,000#	92.5	63.8	87.9	124.3	84.0	115.2	73.6	51.8	72.7
	Hopper car — 175,000#	89.1	42.8	66.8	119.7	56.7	87.8	70.8	34.9	55.7
	Sacramento, Calif.									
Biggs, Calif.	Boxcar — 80,000#		99.7	142.9	158.5	119.3	171.1		118.4	172.4
	Hopper car — 100,000#	126.5	106.4	150.6		128.1	180.0	152.4	126.7	180.6
	Hopper car — 175,000#	120.5	72.8	116.9	150.5	87.7	139.5	147.4	87.8	141.7

TABLE 7-8. (Continued)

		Southeastern markets						Western markets		
		Savannah, Ga.			Miami, Fla.			San Francisco, Calif.		
Drying point	Milling point	Revenue	Out of pocket cost	Fully distributed cost	Revenue	Out of pocket cost	Fully distributed cost	Revenue	Out of pocket cost	Fully distributed cost
					Cents					
	Stuttgart, Ark.									
McGehee, Ark.	Boxcar — 80,000#	66.8	40.8	57.0	85.0	51.1	72.1	—	90.6	131.8
	Hopper car — 100,000#	65.4	40.4	56.6	83.3	51.6	72.5	88.5	96.8	138.0
	Hopper car — 175,000#	63.1	27.0	43.1	80.4	34.9	55.7	81.4	66.4	107.5
	Crowley, La.									
Mermentau, La.	Boxcar — 80,000#	66.3	42.5	59.5	80.0	50.4	71.0	—	92.6	134.6
	Hopper car — 100,000#	64.8	42.4	59.4	78.3	50.9	71.5	85.5	98.5	140.5
	Hopper car — 175,000#	62.3	28.4	45.2	75.4	34.4	54.8	78.4	68.0	109.8
	Houston, Tex.									
Dayton, Tex.	Boxcar — 80,000#	69.5	48.1	67.7	85.5	56.0	79.2	—	86.3	125.2
	Hopper car — 100,000#	67.9	48.8	68.4	84.7	57.3	80.5	77.5	91.4	130.3
	Hopper car — 175,000#	65.1	32.8	52.3	81.6	38.8	61.9	73.8	62.9	101.7
	Sacramento, Calif.									
Biggs, Calif.	Boxcar — 80,000#		115.6	168.3		123.5	179.8		25.9	34.6
	Hopper car — 100,000#	146.0	123.7	176.3	162.8	132.2	188.4	35.5	22.7	31.4
	Hopper car — 175,000#	141.0	85.7	138.3	157.8	91.7	147.9	35.5	13.9	22.6

¹Railroad rates (or revenue) are from published tariffs and reflect transit privileges and charges where applicable. Out-of-pocket and fully distributed costs were computed from: ICC Statement 7-67 "Rail Carload Unit Costs by Territories for the year 1965." Mileage figures used for computations are a combination of short line plus 28300 mileage scale plus 13 percent for circuity factor. Note: Each rate shown is the sum of a rate on dried rough rice from drying point to milling point plus the rate on milled rice to consuming markets. They are the lowest carload rates available and reflect transit privileges and charges where applicable.

profit margins, or perhaps better stated "allowance for return," widening as carloading becomes heavier.

Generally, the revenue received by the railroads for transporting rice from the Southern States to all destination markets, except California, exceeded fully distributed costs for all weight categories by a substantial margin. The percentage relationships are shown in Table 7-9. For rice moving from the South to California, revenues did not cover fully distributed cost for any weight category, and only covered out-of-pocket cost on the heaviest, or 175,000 pounds, example.

California rice shippers presently have a revenue versus cost advantage over Southern shippers. This advantage is evident for all destination markets. The comparisons show that only on the heaviest carloading do California originating revenues meet or exceed (then only slightly) fully distributed costs.

Profitability of Rail Rates on Rice

Although current railroad rates are lower than truck rates, they generally are still quite profitable to the carriers. Table 7-9 illustrates that the revenue received by the railroads from the carload movement of rice from all origins—Arkansas, Louisiana, Texas and California—to Chicago, New York City and Miami in 1965 ranged from 123 percent to 230 percent of out-of-pocket costs and from 86 percent to 147 percent of fully distributed costs.[3] The percentage relationships indicate that rate levels from California to New York are least profitable to the railroads while the Arkansas rate level is most profitable. The rate levels from Louisiana and Texas follow close behind Arkansas in terms of the percentage that revenue is above costs.

Generally, the carriers' rates for all rice producing regions are such that revenues exceed both out-of-pocket and fully distributed costs. It also appears that the heavier the carloading the more profitable the rate from the standpoint of the rail carriers. This is indicated by the much higher percentage of revenue over either out-of-pocket or fully distributed costs for the 175,000 pound hopper car compared to the 80,000 pound box car. Rice shippers, in particularly the southern rice area—Texas, Louisiana, Arkansas and Mississippi—should explore the possibilities for rate reductions based on rail revenue relationships to out-of-pocket costs. Recent Interstate Commerce Commission decisions relating to grains specifically and pertaining to revenues versus out-of-pocket costs indicate that grain rates at a

---

[3]Computation of out-of-pocket and fully distributed costs are for the year 1965 (latest data available). They are compared to rail freight rates in effect July 1967—rates have remained unchanged since 1965.

TABLE 7-9. REVENUE AS A PERCENT OF OUT-OF-POCKET AND FULLY DISTRIBUTED COST FOR RICE FROM SELECTED SOUTHERN AND CALIFORNIA POINTS TO PRINCIPAL MARKETS, RAIL, 1965[1]

From	Percentage relationship of revenue to							
	Out-of-pocket cost				Fully distributed cost			
	Chicago, Ill.	New York, N.Y.	Miami, Fla.	San Francisco, Calif.	Chicago, Ill.	New York, N.Y.	Miami, Fla.	San Francisco, Calif.
	Percent							
Boxcar—80,000 #								
Arkansas	149	167	166	—	107	121	118	—
Louisiana	148	164	159	—	105	118	113	—
Texas	145	160	153	—	103	115	108	—
California								
Covered hopper—100,000 #								
Arkansas	147	157	161	91	106	115	115	41
Louisiana	141	152	154	87	101	111	110	61
Texas	138	148	148	85	98	108	105	59
California	130	124	123	156	91	88	86	113
Covered hopper—175,000 #								
Arkansas	215	226	230	123	136	147	144	76
Louisiana	202	218	219	115	127	140	138	71
Texas	197	211	210	117	124	136	132	73
California	170	172	172	255	104	108	107	157

[1]Out-of-pocket and fully distributed cost were considered as 100 percent cost in each of the computations with revenue being a normally greater percentage of that figure.

166

level of 120 to 125 percent of out-of-pocket costs are compensatory to the railroads.[4]

Transit and Other Privileges

Transit Privileges

One significant characteristic of the railroad rate structure for rice in the South is the system of "transit privileges." This term is used for shipments originating in Louisiana and Texas, while "cut-back" rates refer to a similar system of rate-making in Arkansas. Under transit privileges, a shipment of rice can be halted up to a limited number of times, generally twice, for warehousing or milling or both, and then reshipped to destination at a total charge for all movements. Such a change is generally less than the sum of the rates for the individual movements that are involved. Transit privileges are not available for all points between which movement might take place. However, such privileges are generally available for the principal movements of rice.

In the case of transit privileges from Texas or Louisiana, a "through" rate is available to cover both inbound and outbound movements, generally over the same rail line within 12 months of each other.

In the cut-back rates from Arkansas, there are no through rates covering both inbound and outbound movements. Instead, the rate on the inbound movement of rough rice is reduced by a partial refund. To obtain this refund there must be a corresponding outbound shipment of milled rice under specified conditions.

Some Details of the Operation of Transit Privileges

In Louisiana and Texas, rates on individual movements must be paid when shipments are made. Transit claims are then filed by shippers with railroads separately for each outbound car for the difference between the payments made and the through rate plus the transit charge. A separate claim is required for each end product, viz., milled rice, hulls, etc.

In Arkansas, claims may be filed either on individual shipments or on an annual basis covering all shipments regardless of destination. If shippers post sufficient bond with originating lines for rough rice, they can obtain the net rate on individual shipments. Documentary

[4]*Grain in Multiple-Car Shipments—River Crossings to the South*, 325 I.C.C. 752, page 770 (1965).
"The average relation of revenue to cost for all of the many routes shown would be 118 percent; it would increase to 125 percent for the 500-net ton shipments contemplated by the Southern. See 318 I.C.C. at 716-717. We believe that in a widespread adjustment such as the one here each and every rate need not return something above out-of-pocket costs so long as on an overall basis the rates in the adjustment are compensatory. Especially is this so where the purpose of the proposed rates is to meet unregulated truck competition . . ."

proof of outbound movements via the lines handling the inbound rough rice must be submitted at the time of annual settlement.

The milling process results in shrinkage and some actual waste. This fact is taken into account by transit regulations for shipments originating in Texas or Louisiana. Under these regulations, for every 100 pounds of dried rough rice received by a mill the following maximum quantities may be reshipped under transit privileges: Milled rice (including brewers' or broken), 68 pounds; hulls, 19 pounds; bran, 9 pounds; and polish, 2 pounds. The remaining 2 pounds is considered as the approximate amount of waste or shrinkage, and hence no reshipment under transit privileges is allowed. Milled rice is generally shipped much longer distances than are hulls and other by-products.

In contrast, the system of cut-back rates in Arkansas permits shipping out 100 pounds of any end product or group of end products for every 100 pounds of dried rough rice received. Thus, as much as 100 pounds of milled rice may be shipped for every 100 pounds of dried rough rice received.

In all of the southern states covered by this study, lower rates under transit privileges are available usually if the same railroad line is used for the outbound movement as for the inbound movement. Thus, the system of transit tends to induce not merely the all-rail shipment of rice, but shipment by the same railroad line.

Transit charges are made for movements under transit privileges originating in Texas or Louisiana. These charges are typically paid at the same time that the charges for the outbound movement are paid. There are no transit charges for shipments under cut-back rates from Arkansas.

When either transit privileges or cut-back rates are used, the rate adjustment is applied to the *outbound* rate from the transit point, for example, the location of the rice mill. However, the prospect of this adjustment might be reflected to some degree in prices paid by the mill, and hence the shipper who pays the freight charges from the milling point does not necessarily get all of the benefit from this feature of the railroad rate system.

In California, the rate structure is generally based on maximum carloadings without transit or other privileges. These rates are a "bare bones" type rate, with low rates associated with heavy carloadings. "Bare bones" rail rates are generally predicated on the use of large covered hopper cars designed to haul in excess of 100 tons or over 3,300 bushels of rice. These jumbo hopper cars must move in multiple lots hauling not less than 450 tons. This rate structure does not normally include provisions for storage or milling-in-transit, stops for inspection, indirect routing or reconsignment

168

privileges. In addition, time allowed for loading or unloading cars is not to exceed 24 hours.

Texas Motor Carrier Law — Intrastate

Louisiana and Arkansas do not regulate intrastate motor freight rates on exempt agricultural commodities. However, the States of Texas and California do regulate all "motor-propelled freight vehicles" engaged in transporting property for hire over the public highways, including those hauling exempt agricultural commodities. The Railroad Commission of Texas is the governing body charged with administration of the law and rules in Texas. These laws and rules are very similar to laws and rules established by the Interstate Commerce Commission for regulation of interstate vehicles. Certificates or "permits" are required by all for legal operation of trucks in Texas. The commission regulates rates, insurance needs and equipment to be used; it also oversees accounts, hours of work, safety measures and many other facets of motortruck operation.

Truck rates on rice are slightly higher in Texas and California than in Louisiana or Arkansas.

COMPARATIVE TRANSPORTATION SYSTEMS

Methods of Transporting Rice

Green Rice

Rice harvested by combines is generally high in moisture and cannot be stored without severe losses. Consequently, green rice must be dried in mechanical driers within a few hours after harvest and driers typically are located in close proximity to harvest areas for quick movement. Hence, practically all of the green rice received by the driers was transported by trucks from the farm—trucks normally owned by the producers.

Dried Rough Rice

Information obtained from mill operators in the principal rice producing states showed wide variations in the percentages of rice shipped by rail and truck from driers to mills during 1966 (Table 7-10).

TABLE 7-10. ESTIMATED PERCENTAGES OF RICE SHIPPED BY TRUCK AND RAIL FROM DRIERS TO MILLS FOR ARKANSAS, LOUISIANA, TEXAS AND CALIFORNIA, 1966 SEASON

State	Truck	Rail
	— — — — — Percent — — — — —	
Arkansas	20	80
Louisiana	70	30
Texas	45	55
California	90	10

The differences among states in amount of dried rice moving by rail or truck from driers to mills is generally due to the operational structure and methods of the rice industry in each state.

Most Arkansas rice is handled by firms who have geared their operations to bulk handling by rail using an assigned fleet of railroad-owned covered hopper cars dispatched by the firms in shuttle service between driers and mills. This is possible because the firms have integrated vertically from driers through milling, largely through the use of a cooperative structure.

In Texas and Louisiana rice firms are generally not vertically integrated. Consequently, a controlled rail shuttle movement using assigned cars from driers to mills is not as workable and has not been used as extensively. Hence, less reliance is placed on intra-area rail movement in these states.

The industry in the Gulf area should explore the potentials of developing coordinating arrangements between vertically integrated driers and mills which would permit controlled rail transportation between these facilities.

California mills also depend primarily on trucks rather than rail to move rice from driers to mills. This is due to closer proximity of driers to mills and the greater flexibility of trucks which permit faster and more efficient movements in this producing region.

Milled Rice

According to estimates of mill managers, over 90 percent of all interstate shipments of milled rice move to domestic markets by rail. Estimates for Louisiana and Texas were 90 percent; Arkansas, 95 percent; and for California, 99 percent.

California ships almost half of its milled rice in bulk to domestic markets as well as to export markets. For Arkansas, 25 percent of export shipments and 90 percent of domestic shipments moves in bulk while from Louisiana and Texas only 2 percent and 1 percent, respectively, move in bulk.

Rail Equipment Used

Covered hopper rail cars have many advantages over boxcars for bulk movement of rice by rail. Arkansas cooperatives moved about 90 percent of both inbound and domestic outbound rail shipments to and from mills in covered hopper cars. California cooperatives moved about 50 percent of their rail inbound rice to mills and 75 percent of their rail outbound milled rice shipments in covered hopper cars. Covered hopper cars are not being used to any great extent in Louisiana and Texas.

Louisiana and Texas rice shippers should explore the possibilities of moving more rice in bulk by covered hopper cars and of maximizing loading while foregoing transit privileges and other fringe benefits.

Covered hopper cars have several distinct advantages over box-cars in bulk movement of rice when rail is the most feasible method of transportation. The most notable of these are that covered hopper cars have little leakage or contamination, they reduce the time and labor requirements for loading and unloading, and they permit heavier loads and thus opportunities for reduced rates.

The Arkansas Rice Growers Association reported that they have an assigned fleet of covered hopper cars. Basically, this means that the rail carrier originating shipments sets up a pool of hopper cars, assigning a specified number of cars to the mill for use in shuttle-type service. Under this arrangement the mill has an assured supply of cars with control of these cars under its jurisdiction.

Privately Operated Motortrucks

Only one of the cooperatives interviewed reported ownership of trucks; none reported leasing arrangements. The cooperative that owned trucks used them primarily for small-order, drop delivery service.

All other trucking services necessary to the individual cooperative operations were obtained from exempt or common carrier trucks. Truck brokers were used by the cooperatives for nearly all exempt truck movements. Common carriers hauled rice only occasionally, and then only when they needed backhauls.

Pattern of Rice Movements by Rail

The waybill statistics compiled by the Interstate Commerce Commission provide data on the State-to-State movement of rice by railroads. Illustrations are for two periods, 1948-53 and 1959-63 (Tables 7-11 and 7-12). A reasonably accurate picture of such movements is presented considering limitations of the data.

Of the regions in which no rice production or milling of consequence takes place, the East North Central region (consisting of Ohio, Indiana, Illinois, Michigan and Wisconsin) had the largest volume of rail receipts of rice for both periods, 1948-53 and 1959-63. Of the total rail receipts in that region (probably consisting almost exclusively of milled rice for table use and for manufacturing), 75 percent originated in the southern rice states in 1948-53, while only 49 percent originated in the southern rice states in 1959-63. Most of the remainder came from California for both periods.

Of the total rice receipts in the East North Central region, Louisiana accounted for 31 percent during 1948-53 and only about

TABLE 7-11. RAILROAD MOVEMENTS OF RICE: 1 PERCENT SAMPLE OF CARLOAD WAYBILLS BY TERMINATION REGION ACCORDING TO STATE OR REGION OF ORIGIN, 1959-63 TOTALS

	Termination region[1]									
State or region of origin	North Atlantic		East North Central		West North Central		Southern states other than rice states		United States[2]	
	Tons	Percentage of total	Tons	Percentage of total	Tons	Percentage of total	Tons	Percentage of total	Tons	Percentage of total
Southern rice states										
Arkansas	370	19.6	1,169	32.6	349	26.6	1,048	37.0	30,219	41.1
Louisiana	171	9.1	312	8.7	315	24.0	1,168	41.2	15,918	21.6
Mississippi	0	0	0	0	146	11.2	0	0	1,247	1.7
Texas	118	6.2	263	7.3	243	18.5	585	20.7	20,385	27.7
Total	659	34.9	1,744	48.6	1,053	80.3	2,801	98.9	67,769	92.1
California	479	25.4	1,818	50.7	258	19.7	0	0	4,993	6.8
Other States	748	39.7	24	.7	0	0	31	1.1	803	1.1
United States	1,886	100.0	3,586	100.0	1,311	100.0	2,832	100.0	73,565	100.0

[1]The composition of the specified regions is as follows: *North Atlantic*—New England plus New York, New Jersey, Pennsylvania; *East North Central*—Ohio, Indiana, Illinois, Michigan, Wisconsin; *West North Central*—Minnesota, Iowa, Missouri, North Dakota, South Dakota, Nebraska, Kansas; *Southern rice states*—Arkansas, Louisiana, Mississippi, Tennessee, Texas; *Southern States other than rice states*—Delaware, Maryland, District of Columbia, Virginia, West Virginia, North Carolina, South Carolina, Georgia, Florida, Kentucky, Alabama, Oklahoma. The ICC omits Tennessee from the waybill sample of rice movements because it has fewer than 3 shippers.
[2]Includes all regions of the United States, not merely those shown in table.
Source: Interstate Commerce Commission, *Carload Waybill Statistics.*

TABLE 7-12. RAILROAD MOVEMENTS OF RICE: 1 PERCENT SAMPLE OF CARLOAD WAYBILLS BY TERMINATION REGION ACCORDING TO STATE OR REGION OF ORIGIN, 1948-53 TOTALS

| State or region of origin | Termination region[1] | | | | | | | | United States[2] | |
| | North Atlantic | | East North Central | | West North Central | | Southern States other than rice states | | | |
	Tons	Percentage of total	Tons	Percentage of total	Tons	Percentage of total	Tons	Percentage of total	Tons	Percentage of total
Southern rice states										
Arkansas	666	26.2	2,064	27.1	596	31.4	3,711	55.8	21,304	23.9
Louisiana	220	8.7	2,396	31.4	423	22.3	1,465	22.0	23,633	26.4
Mississippi	0	0	0	0	0	0	42	0.6	512	0.6
Texas	446	17.5	1,290	16.9	402	21.1	1,387	20.8	35,184	39.4
Total	1,332	52.4	5,750	75.4	1,421	74.8	6,605	99.2	80,633	90.3
California	261	10.3	1,432	18.8	480	25.2	50	0.8	7,275	8.1
Other states	949	37.3	446	5.8	0	0	0	0	1,395	1.6
United States	2,542	100.0	7,628	100.0	1,901	100.0	6,655	100.0	89,303	100.0

[1]The composition of the specified regions is as follows: *North Atlantic*—New England plus New York, New Jersey, Pennsylvania; *East North Central*—Ohio, Indiana, Illinois, Michigan, Wisconsin; *West North Central*—Minnesota, Iowa, Missouri, North Dakota, South Dakota, Nebraska, Kansas; *Southern rice states*—Arkansas, Louisiana, Mississippi, Tennessee, Texas; *Southern States other than rice states*—Delaware, Maryland, District of Columbia, Virginia, West Virginia, North Carolina, South Carolina, Georgia, Florida, Kentucky, Alabama, Oklahoma. The ICC omits Tennessee from the waybill sample of rice movements because it has fewer than 3 shippers.

[2]Includes all regions of the United States, not merely those shown in table.

Source: Interstate Commerce Commission, *Carload Waybill Statistics.*

9 percent during 1959-63. Arkansas accounted for 27 percent for 1948-53 and about 33 percent for 1959-63. Texas accounted for 17 percent during the first period, and only 7 percent during the second period.

Approximately half of the 1948-53 receipts in the North Atlantic region (consisting of New England, New York, New Jersey and Pennsylvania) came from the southern rice region during 1948-53, while only about one-third came from the southern region during 1959-63. California furnished only 10 percent of the receipts for the early period but over 25 percent for the latter period.

The relatively large volume of receipts (37 and 39 percent, respectively, for the two periods) that came from the same or other North Atlantic States which do not grow or mill rice can be explained by water-rail movements—water from the Gulf to North Atlantic ports and rail movements beyond.

Rail carload weights have been steadily increasing over the years. Table 7-13 shows average tons of rice per rail carload originated in the southwestern, southern and western regions as reported by the Interstate Commerce Commission.

The average net weight of rice per rail car shipped from the southwestern region was slightly over 51 tons in 1963.[5] This was over 90 percent higher than the average of 26 tons in 1929. The southern and western regions are characterized by similar increased carloadings over the years with the southern region in 1963 being 88 percent over the 1929 average, and the western region 85 percent over 1929.

[5] Later year comparisons are not possible due to the new classifications for reporting as instituted by the Interstate Commerce Commission for 1964.

TABLE 7-13. AVERAGE TONS OF RICE PER RAIL CARLOAD ORIGINATED IN THE SOUTHWESTERN, SOUTHERN AND WESTERN REGIONS, SELECTED YEARS, 1929-65

Year	Average tons per carload			Percent of 1929 average		
	Southwestern	Southern	Western	Southwestern	Southern	Western
	Tons			Percent		
1929	26.2	21.6	26.8	100	100	100
1934	28.3	21.2	28.8	108	98	107
1939	29.3	24.8	30.0	112	115	112
1941	31.0	23.6	31.5	118	109	118
1942	36.9	28.8	36.9	141	133	138
1943	43.7	41.5	43.6	167	192	163
1948	42.5	39.7	42.8	162	184	160
1950	39.3	29.9	39.9	150	138	149
1953	41.2	38.1	42.1	157	176	157
1954	40.8	38.5	41.6	156	178	155
1955	42.4	41.4	42.7	162	192	159
1956	43.3	41.2	43.3	165	191	162
1957	43.2	41.6	43.3	165	193	162
1958	42.7	36.5	42.9	163	169	160
1959	43.9	39.0	44.2	168	181	165
1960	45.5	40.3	45.6	174	187	170
1961	46.6	41.7	46.8	178	193	175
1962	48.9	43.3	48.2	187	200	180
1963	50.1	40.5	49.7	191	188	185
1964[1] (rough rice)	²	48.6	50.8	²	225	190
1964 (milled rice)	²	30.0	48.2	²	139	180
1965 (rough rice)	²	47.0	51.4	²	218	192
1965 (milled rice)	²	31.4	49.1	²	145	183

[1]Prior to 1964 the Interstate Commerce Commission grouped rough rice and milled rice as one commodity in their reports. In 1964 a new classification was established and rough rice shipments were reported separately from milled rice shipments.

²A new regional classification established with the Southwestern region included in the Western region.

Source: Interstate Commerce Commission, *Freight Commodity Statistics.*

175

8

Role of Federal Government In Rice Marketing

Fred H. Tyner

Although the United States produces only about 2 percent of the world's rice, it is currently the leading rice exporting country. Until recently, the United States ranked below Burma, Thailand and a small number of other countries in exports. In 1965, however, U. S. exports comprised about 20 percent of world exports.[1]

For the 1966 crop year, U. S. production was estimated at about 85 million hundredweight of rough rice. Of this production, about 61 percent (52 million hundredweight) was exported.[2] The recent emergence of the United States as a major rice exporter might be construed as an indication that U. S. exporters have become more aggressive and competitive in the world marketplace. While their activity has been a significant factor, the picture would likely be much less bright if it were not for exports under government programs.

These government program exports generate a large share of U. S. rice exports—about 49 percent in 1966. The importance of rice as a world food, and U. S. interest in world food problems indicates that these exports may continue in the future.

The historical role of the government in regulating rice production has received considerable attention, but the less obvious effect on the rice industry of government influence on food aid exports, export subsidies and rice utilization in domestic programs has not been examined so closely.

Because of this involvement of the government, it appears appropriate to examine the impact that its activities have on the U. S. commercial rice market. The level of government exports, the level of export subsidy payments, and the amount of rice utilized in domestic distribution programs—as well as the manner in which these activities are carried out—are all potentially important factors in the functioning of the commercial rice marketing system.

---

[1]*Rice Situation,* USDA, January 1967, p. 10.
[2]*Rice Situation,* USDA, January 1968, p. 2.

MAJOR AREAS OF INFLUENCE

Major governmental influence on the U.S. rice industry is felt through the national program of production controls and price supports. These have been dealt with at some length previously in Chapter 4. Other government activities may, and often do, significantly affect the rice industry, and it is with such activities that this chapter will be largely concerned. The major sources of these influences are Commodity Credit Corporation activities, trade and aid programs and changing government policy objectives.

CCC Activities

The Commodity Credit Corporation functions as the medium through which prices are supported, furnishing price support loans for stored rice and accepting collateral rice as payment for non-recourse loans. Stocks acquired in this manner are used in both domestic and foreign programs. When such stocks are not sufficient to meet the needs of these programs, alternative supplies of rice are required. Rice for domestic distribution programs is procured by purchases on a bid basis. Supplies of rice for export under government programs are obtained through regular commercial channels, with the exports facilitated by government financing.

CCC support through nonrecourse loans became significant in the 1954 crop year, when 47.4 percent of the crop was put under support and 39.1 percent of total production was actually acquired by CCC. Since mid-1954, CCC has acquired over 90 million hundredweight of rice, mostly during the middle and late 1950's. Commodity Credit Corporation acquisitions amounted to 42 percent of the 1955 U.S. rice crop, about 34 percent of the 1956 crop and about one-fourth of the 1957 crop. By 1960, however, acquisitions by CCC had dropped substantially, and they have continued to decline since.

In Table 8-1, the differences between figures in the two columns "placed under price support" and "delivered to CCC" represent loans redeemed by farmers. The accumulation of world rice supplies in 1953 caused the world price to move downward from a record high in the 1952-53 season.[3] This difference between the world price and the higher U.S. support price caused large stocks of rice placed under loan not to be redeemed, as evidenced by the high level of deliveries to CCC in 1954, 1955, 1956 and 1957 especially. Deliveries to CCC in these 4 years ranged from about 26 percent of production to 42 percent of production.

Since 1962, CCC acquisitions have remained below one million hundredweight (rough basis). CCC stocks of rice since 1964 have been below 1 million hundredweight; hence, current commitments cannot

---

[3]*Rice Situation,* November 1956, pp. 5-7.

TABLE 8-1. PRICE SUPPORT OPERATIONS FOR RICE IN TERMS OF ROUGH RICE, COMMODITY CREDIT CORPORATION, 1948-65

Crop of	Placed under price support	Delivered to CCC	Percent of production	Stocks owned by CCC[1]	Loans outstanding[1]
	— — 1,000 cwt. — —			— — 1,000 cwt. — —	
1948	3,718	611	1.6	11	1
1949	8,147	3,043	6.1	459	218
1950	792	26		378	17
1951	5,851	518	1.1	226	1
1952	209			2	6
1953	4,474	3,170	6.1	917	283
1954	30,475	25,141	39.1	15,856	2,589
1955	26,260	23,475	42.0	27,062	312
1956	23,727	16,771	33.9	12,507	48
1957	13,567	11,007	25.6	12,003	9
1958	11,586	6,575	14.7	9,421	34
1959	12,304	7,034	13.1	6,864	3
1960	13,105	4,876	9.0	4,124	8
1961	6,373	34		319	
1962	12,224	1,841	2.7	1,852	8
1963	10,023	771	1.1	1,435	
1964	7,728	787	1.1	1,041	3
1965	9,997	403	0.5	617	7

[1]At marketing year end, July 31.
Source: USDA, *Rice Situation, Rice-Annual Marketing Summary* and *Agricultural Statistics,* various issues.

be met with CCC stocks. As a result, rice exported under government programs has been acquired through the commercial market channels with the U. S. government financing the sales.

The involvement by states in price support operations for recent years is shown in Table 8-2. Rice production is concentrated in Texas, Arkansas, Louisiana and California, with Mississippi and Missouri producing relatively minor amounts. While rather large proportions of the crop have been placed under the loan for the 1962-65 crop years, only a small percentage has ultimately been delivered to CCC. Mississippi has led in percentage of crop delivered in 1963-65, while Louisiana and California have delivered negligible quantities or none at all. These differences reflect such factors as type or variety produced, export shipping facilities available and general availability of processing and marketing facilities.

Government Export Activities

Most of the rice accumulated by CCC has been moved into consumption, chiefly abroad. CCC has sold or otherwise disposed of its owned stocks of rice through five major export outlets: (1) com-

179

TABLE 8-2. RICE: PRODUCTION, QUANTITY PLACED UNDER PRICE SUPPORT, DELIVERIES TO CCC AND MAJOR RICE PRODUCING STATES, CROPS OF 1962-65[1]

State	Production	Placed under support			Deliveries to CCC	Percent of crop	
		Loans	Purchase agreements	Total		Put under support	Delivered to CCC
		– – – – – – 1,000 cwt. – – – – – –			– – –	– – Percent – –	
				Crop of 1962			
Arkansas	16,401	921	1,596	2,517	128	15.3	0.8
California	15,988	3,766		3,766	210	23.6	1.3
Louisiana	15,494	304	346	650	46	4.2	0.3
Mississippi	1,568	630	5	635	49	40.5	3.1
Missouri	193	15	3	18	12	9.3	6.2
Texas	16,401	3,730	906	4,636	1,387	28.3	8.5
				Crop of 1963			
Arkansas	18,105	2,110	1,359	3,469	326	19.2	1.8
California	14,580	11	2,216	2,227		15.3	
Louisiana	16,891	756	423	1,179	4	7.0	
Mississippi	1,911	847	36	883	219	46.2	11.5
Missouri	202	7	1	8	5	4.0	2.5
Texas	18,394	2,157	104	2,261	217	12.3	1.2
				Crop of 1964			
Arkansas	18,490	3,808		3,808	179	20.6	1.0
California	16,023	10		10		0.1	
Louisiana	16,929	279		279	5	1.6	
Mississippi	1,838	838		838	307	45.6	16.7
Missouri	198	2		2	2	1.0	1.0
Texas	19,635	2,693		2,693	290	13.7	1.5
				Crop of 1965			
Arkansas	18,662	6,335		6,335	245	33.9	1.3
California	15,696						
Louisiana	18,798	312		312		1.7	
Mississippi	1,850	842		842	74	45.5	4.0
Missouri	212	1		1			
Texas	21,714	2,314		2,314	75	10.7	0.3

[1]Source: *Rice—Annual Market Summary.*

mercial sales for dollars, (2) payment-in-kind export subsidy, (3) sales for foreign currencies and dollars under Public Law 480,[4] (4) barter and (5) transfers and donations.

Commercial Sales for Dollars

Rough rice from CCC stocks for export is offered for sale to U. S. exporters at announced prices by CCC and in redemption of export certificates. Rice is also sold for unrestricted domestic or export use at not less than the statutory minimum of 5 percent above current support price, plus reasonable carrying charges or other minimum which may be set by CCC to move deteriorating stocks. Section 407 of the Agricultural Act of 1949, as amended, authorizes the sale of CCC-owned commodities for export without price restrictions and includes sales made on condition that commodities of the same kind of comparable value or quantity be exported in raw or processed form.

Subsidized Exports

Historically, CCC has sold or otherwise disposed of its owned stocks of rice largely through programs based on a payment-in-kind export subsidy or through sales for foreign currencies and dollars under PL-480. The beginning date for the payment-in-kind program (PIK) for rice was December 16, 1958. The objective of the PIK program was to enable surplus agricultural commodities to compete in foreign markets, since the U. S. price was higher than the world price. The PIK program also produced a continuing outlet for CCC stocks. In August 1966, the PIK program was discontinued in favor of an Export Payments Program involving cash export subsidies. From the beginning date to August 1966 when the program was discontinued in favor of cash export subsidies, the quantity of rice from commercial stocks earning payment-in-kind certificates amounted to 170.9 million hundredweight. Over the same time interval, the quantity redeemed from CCC stocks amounted to only 9.7 million hundredweight. The certificates were interchangeable and most were redeemed in CCC-owned feed grains instead of rice.

Under the Export Payment Program, the exporter purchases from regular commercial sources the rice he expects to ship and registers his export sale with the U. S. Department of Agriculture. The export payment he receives is based on the quantity and kind of rice exported times an export rate which is announced weekly for the different varieties of rice.

Export subsidies for rice, in effect since December 1958, are intended to move rice into export directly from commercial stocks. Export payment rates are announced weekly by the Department of Agriculture for the following groups of rice: two groups of long- and (5) transfers and donations.

---

[4]Agricultural Trade and Development Assistance Act of 1954.

grain, one group of medium-grain, Pearl and Calrose rice. For milled long-grain rice, the subsidy rate dropped from $2.68 per hundredweight in February 1966 to zero on May 10, 1967. From the latter date until July 4, 1967 there was an export subsidy only for Pearl rice.

The subsidy is necessary when the U. S. domestic price is higher than the world price. There is dissatisfaction in the producing and exporting segments of the rice industry because of the recent drop in subsidy rates. Whether this dissatisfaction is justified depends on whether the "world price" is estimated accurately. Because rice is a staple food in the primary producing countries only a small percentage of production enters world trade. Hence, it is difficult to measure a meaningful world price.

Foreign Currency Sales

Sales for local currencies under PL-480 account for substantial quantities of U. S. agricultural commodities. This program began with the Agricultural Trade and Development Assistance Act of 1954 and was extended for 1967 and 1968 by the "Food for Peace" Act of 1966. Transactions involving payment in local currencies require the following steps:[5]

1. Agreement by a foreign country to purchase U. S. agricultural commodities and pay for them with foreign currencies.
2. Application for purchase authorizations and dollar financing, and issuance of letters of commitment by CCC to U. S. banks.
3. Purchase of commodities from a U. S. exporter. The importer pays in foreign currency at the foreign bank and the exporter receives payment in dollars at the U. S. bank.
4. CCC reimburses the U. S. bank and the foreign bank deposits the foreign currency payment to the U. S. account in the foreign currency.

In brief, the USDA issues a purchase authorization which, upon being signed by the importing country, is publicly announced. The resulting transaction is handled like any other commercial grain transaction, except that the price must have the approval of the Office of the General Sales Manager, USDA.

Requirements (exports) under this category are highly variable from year to year because they are directly related to our trade policies with individual countries. The factors which determine our trade patterns with specific countries operate to influence the quantity of exports and their timing. This irregularity appears to be a significant factor in the operation of the domestic rice market. U. S. exports of milled rice for local currencies, 1959-65, are given by country of destination in Table 8-3.

[5]From USDA, *ASCS Background Information No. 3*, October 1966.

Long-Term Credit

PL-480 also provides that long-term supply and dollar credit sales agreements may be entered into with U. S. or foreign traders and governments of friendly nations. Emphasis in the agreements is on the use of credit to expand dollar markets for U. S. farm products, to develop foreign markets for these products and to assist in the economic development of friendly nations.

Under this legislation, the President may enter into long-term supply and credit arrangements with the governments of friendly nations. The Secretary of Agriculture may enter into similar agreements with the United States or foreign private trade. Such agreements may provide for delivery of U. S. surplus agricultural commodities over periods up to 10 years. Dollar repayment over periods of up to 20 years is authorized.

Financing and operational procedures for long-term credit sales are generally similar to those for local currency sales—with the exception that payment is made in dollars instead of foreign currency. The

TABLE 8-3. RICE, MILLED: U.S. EXPORTS FOR FOREIGN CURRENCY (PL-480) BY COUNTRY OF DESTINATION, 1959-65[1]

Country of destination	Year beginning July						
	1959	1960	1961	1962	1963	1964	1965
	— — — — — — — — 1,000 cwt. — — — — — — — —						
Argentina	60						
Bolivia			61				
Ceylon	904						
Congo			272	309	661	698	896
Egypt	934						
Ghana							387
Guinea			280	538	919	347	413
Iceland	6	4	7	4	4	3	
India	3,776	6,006	3,048	5,975	8,027	7,216	224
Indonesia	3,278	2,677	3,318	5,608	1,958		
Israel	110	108	86	152	108	76	65
Ivory Coast					234	222	
Pakistan	320	2,850					
Peru	480				558		
Philippines					404	2,068	824
Poland				110	238		
Senegal					523		
Syria			255				
Turkey		228					
Vietnam			919			557	4,395
Total	9,868	11,873	8,246	12,696	13,634	11,187	7,204

[1]Total exports for earlier years are (in 1,000 cwt.): 1955—2,530; 1956—18,020; 1957—5,049; and 1958—3,883.

Source: *Rice Situation,* January 1967, p. 27.

first government-to-government long-term credit agreement was made in August 1961. From that time through June 1966, agreements have been entered into with 31 foreign countries, involving an estimated export market value, excluding ocean transportation costs of $712 million of U. S. agricultural commodities.

Table 8-4 shows long-term credit sales exports of milled rice by country of destination. As of June 1966, exports had not been made to about two dozen countries with which agreements had been made.

Barter

Barter transactions are carried out through regular commercial channels by private U. S. firms. Since 1949, large quantities of CCC-owned farm products have been "swapped" for strategic and other materials produced abroad. More recently, substantial quantities of farm products have been bartered predominantly for the procurement abroad of materials, goods, equipment and services for U. S. agencies which reimburse CCC rather than spending those dollars abroad. By reducing the need for dollar expenditures abroad by these U. S. agencies, the balance of payments is helped. However, barter transactions involving rice have been relatively minor.

Donations

Food commodities in excess of anticipated domestic dispositions may be donated to nonprofit voluntary agencies registered with the Advisory Committee on Voluntary Foreign Aid, or to other appropriate department or agency of the federal government, and to intergovernmental organizations for use in the assistance of needy persons outside the United States. The Agency for International Development receives substantial quantities of CCC-owned farm products under PL-480 for (1) famine, disaster relief, or extraordinary relief requirements and (2) to promote economic and community development through assistance programs undertaken with friendly governments or through voluntary relief agencies. Annual donations of

TABLE 8-4. RICE, MILLED: U.S. EXPORTS FOR LONG TERM CREDIT (PL-480) BY COUNTRY OF DESTINATION, 1962-65

Country of destination		Year beginning July		
	1962	1963	1964	1965
	— — — — — — 1,000 cwt. — — — — — —			
Dominican Republic	716.5	668.0	487.0	
Liberia	52.9			109.8
Nansei and Nonop Islands		487.2	448.0	
Iceland			203.0	
Ivory Coast			236.0	516.9
Indonesia				89.3
Total	769.4	1,155.2	1,374.0	716.0

Source: Foreign Agricultural Service, USDA.

184

rice averaged about 1.2 million hundredweight (milled) over 1955-61, but rice was not involved in the donation program for 1961-66.

Summary of Government Exports

Table 8-5 shows exports of milled rice under specified government programs. During 1948-1966, the percentage of total U. S. milled rice exported varied from a relatively low proportion of 36.9 percent during 1952-55 to 57.8 percent during 1962-65. Rough rice exports averaged less than 200,000 hundredweight during 1962-65, while milled rice exports averaged 29,200,000 hundredweight during the same period.

With the beginning of heavy CCC activities during the mid-1950's, the proportion of U. S. rice exports under specified government programs rose from 3.7 percent in 1954-55 to a high of 82.9 percent in 1956-57, with 69 percent in this latter period for local currencies alone.

The data in Table 8-5 separating government program exports into local currency sales and long-term credit sales, exhibit considerable variability. PL-480 exports are theoretically limited to the "annual availability" or the excess over domestic requirements, adequate carry-over and the normal level of commercial exports. Pressing needs for rice in the interest of foreign relations may take precedence over these accepted guidelines, however. The effect of such an occurrence, and especially the timing of PL-480 procurements, may be relatively minor on the industry as an entirety but could pose a considerable number of decision-making problems for individual firms.

CHANGE U. S. COMMERCIAL EXPORT POSITION

In 1956-57, the record exports of 26.3 million hundredweight milled rice equivalent included about 6.9 million hundredweight of commercial exports. In 1957-58, total exports declined to about 12.1 million hundredweight, with slightly over half moving under government programs.[6]

Exports of milled rice "outside government programs" for the marketing years 1956-66 are given in Table 8-6. These exports "outside government programs" include, in addition to unassisted commercial transactions, shipments with government assistance in the form of extension of credit, sales of government-owned rice at less than domestic market prices and export payments in cash or kind.

Table 8-7 shows commercial exports by countries for the years 1959-65. Totals are slightly different than in Table 8-6 because they are on a July-June year rather than the August-July rice marketing year.

---

[6]These figures are reported on a marketing year basis, and thus are slightly different from the fiscal year totals in Table 6.

TABLE 8-5. U.S. EXPORTS OF MILLED RICE UNDER SPECIFIED GOVERNMENT-FINANCED PROGRAMS, JULY-JUNE 1954-66

| Fiscal year | PL-480 | | | | | PL-655 See 402, sales for foreign currency and economic aid | Total Exports under specified government programs | Total exports | |
	Sales for foreign currency	Famine and other emergency relief	Foreign donation[1]	Barter[2]	Long term credit			Quantity	Percent under specified government programs
	1,000 cwt.								
1954-55	—	—	—	5	—	1	311	8,443	3.7
1955-56	2,530	305	865	195		563	6,089	11,575	52.6
1956-57	18,127	1,943	2,175	657		248	21,756	26,244	82.9
1957-58	5,094	549	596	8		153	6,334	11,797	53.7
1958-59	3,767	483	541	2,552			6,900	14,020	49.2
1959-60	9,960	40	1,417	683		162	12,797	20,232	63.2
1960-61	11,906	575	1,751	348		93	14,502	21,204	68.4
1961-62	8,612	404				494	9,546	20,333	46.9
1962-63	12,742	440			770	341	13,867	24,054	57.6
1963-64	13,211	14			1,072	593	14,876	31,690	46.9
1964-65	11,004				759	38	11,801	28,487	41.4
1965-66	6,917				716	2,008	9,641	30,324	31.8

[1]Foreign donations are authorized under Section 416 of the Agricultural Act of 1949 and Section 302, Title III, Public law 480.
[2]The barter program is authorized under the Charter Act of the Commodity Credit Corporation, Section 303, Title III, Public law 480, and other legislation.

Source: USDA, Rice: Annual Market Summary, 1961-66 issues.

TABLE 8-6. COMMERCIAL EXPORTS OF MILLED RICE, U.S., 1956-66

Marketing year	Commercial exports
	1,000 cwt.
1956-57	6,900
1957-58	5,929
1958-59	7,120
1959-60	7,435
1960-61	6,720
1961-62	10,787
1962-63	10,187
1963-64	16,814
1964-65	16,686
1965-66	20,683

Source: *Rice, Annual Marketing Summary.*

In December 1958, the payment-in-kind program was passed to encourage the movement of rice into export directly from commercial stocks. Commercial exports for 1958-59 moved up from 5.9 million hundredweight to about 7.4 million hundredweight, milled rice basis. The year's most important development was the sharp increase in shipments to European destinations, largely as a result of the payment-in-kind program.

In the year ending June 30, 1960, U. S. rice export sales for dollars—mainly to Europe, Cuba and Africa—were the largest since 1955. The United States also ranked fourth in world rice trade, next to Burma, Thailand and Communist China.

TABLE 8-7. RICE, MILLED: U.S. EXPORTS UNDER COMMERCIAL TERMS BY COUNTRY OF DESTINATION, 1959-65

Country of destination	Year beginning July						
	1959	1960	1961	1962	1963	1964	1965
	— — — — — — 1,000 cwt. — — — — — —
EEC	901	1,910	2,778	1,938	2,198	1,455	2,063
Other	597	750	1,111	1,391	1,391	1,305	2,140
Total Western Europe	1,498	2,660	3,889	3,329	3,589	2,760	4,203
Canada	284	233	664	904	1,036	1,100	958
Cuba	3,183	402					
Japan	2	2	1	31	2,264	4,308	5,447
Republic of South Africa	299	766	945	1,025	1,268	1,211	1,586
Other	2,708	3,113	5,712	5,106	8,305	6,657	8,302
Total	7,974	7,176	11,211	10,395	16,462	16,036	20,496

Source: *Rice Situation,* various issues.

Lower exports for dollars in 1960-61 reflected the loss of the Cuban market. In 1961-62 exports for dollars rose from 7.2 million hundredweight to 11.2 million hundredweight, with large increases in commercial sales to Africa and Europe. Commercial exports in 1962-63 were about 10.2 million hundredweight but increased to 16.8 million hundredweight in 1963-64, all of which moved under CCC export payments in cash or in kind. Commercial exports were decreased slightly in 1964-65, but accounted for over half of total exports.

"Dollar sales" hit an all-time high of 20.1 million hundredweight in 1965-66 and accounted for two-thirds of total rice exports. In terms of total exports, shipments to the Dominican Republic, Peru and Ecuador decline, while shipments to Mexico, Jamaica, El Salvador, the French West Indies and Honduras picked up. The Netherlands, France, West Germany and Switzerland took substantially larger shipments while Poland dropped out of the market entirely after taking fairly large quantities in most recent years. Exports to India were down 7.4 million hundredweight, but shipments to Vietnam increased by 7.3 million hundredweight. Japan remained the largest single Asian customer for U. S. rice.

IMPACT ON OTHER PRODUCING COUNTRIES

During the postwar period the United States has played a leading role in attempting to bring about a greater degree of freedom in international trade. The attempts involve assistance in connection with the rehabilitation of the economies of countries affected by World War II, and through leadership in the General Agreement on Tariffs and Trade (GATT).

Until recently, price supports have resulted in U. S. domestic rice prices considerably higher than the export price that most importing countries could offer, thus pricing U. S. rice out of the export market. Therefore, the U. S. government provided an export payment on virtually all commercial sales of rice for export.

In addition to these subsidized exports for dollars, disposal of surplus rice has been carried out by a variety of programs, including sales for foreign currencies, gifts to meet emergency requirements and to promote economic development in underdeveloped areas, donations through nonprofit voluntary agencies and international organizations, barter transactions and sales for dollars on long-term credit. Sizable quantities of rice have moved in this manner, and competing exporters argue that their export trade has been affected. Whether this is true to a significant degree is questionable, however, because of the lack of purchasing power prevalent in many recipient countries. In the case of donations, for example, program plans, requests and operations are reviewed by coordinating committees composed of representatives of the U. S. mission or consulate and voluntary agencies. Assurances are obtained that the relief program does not conflict with normal commercial trade.

Barter program rules have provided, since November 1958, that the national interest of the United States will not be adversely affected, usual U. S. marketings will be safeguarded and undue disruption of world price or replacement of cash sales for dollars will not occur.

DOMESTIC DISTRIBUTION PROGRAMS

Domestic distribution of rice is made to nonprofit school lunch programs, needy Indians on reservations, charitable institutions serving needy persons, disaster organizations and state and local welfare agencies. In donating foods for domestic distribution the USDA arranges for and finances processing or packaging of the commodities and pays transportation costs to central receiving locations in the various states. At the state level the program is administered by agencies operating under agreements with the USDA. The state agencies, with responsibility for the certification of eligible recipients, order commodities and arrange for the receipt and storage of commodities and their ultimate distribution to eligible recipients.

Under various legislative authorities, CCC may donate dairy products to the Veteran's Administration for use in its hospitals, and to the Secretary of the Army for use in Army, Navy and Air Force rations, including hospital rations in addition to their normal market purchases; donate food commodities to federal penal and correctional institutions for minors; and make commodities available for relief in distressed areas.

Domestic donations of rice (milled) since 1959 have ranged from 1.0 million hundredweight to 1.4 million hundredweight. Because of low CCC stocks in recent years, the majority of these needs since mid-1962 have been met by purchases in the commercial market. These requirements have been relatively stable and should, therefore, have little unsettling influence on the industry. Data on domestic donations and purchases in the commercial market are given in Table 8-8.

GOVERNMENT MARKETING ACTIVITY AND PRICING EFFICIENCY

Because the rice producing industry has operated under acreage controls since 1954, the decision as to the acreage of rice which a farmer will plant is not particularly difficult to make. The major decisions in attempting to make a profit at the farm level are those related to lowering per unit production costs and selling at the highest possible price.

The following discussion is concerned with factors that influence the price farmers and higher market levels receive for their rice, especially with reference to government decisions.

TABLE 8-8. RICE, MILLED: DOMESTIC DONATIONS BY RECIPIENT AGENCY AND PURCHASES IN THE COMMERCIAL MARKET IN PARENTHESES

Fiscal year	Schools	Institutions	Needy persons	Total
		— — — — — — — — 1,000 cwt. — — — — — — — —		
1955	67	46	115	228
1956	174	94	235	503
1957	219	108	476	803
1958	198	87	563	848
1959	200	120	808	1,128
1960	212	93	695	1,000
1961	219	85	864	1,168
1962	222	82	1,109	1,413
1963	(57)219	(74)74	(855) 943	(986)1,236
1964	(50)250	(58)89	(991)1,016	(1,099)1,355
1965	256	(119)97	(969) 951	(1,088)1,304
1966	307	(68)91	(726) 807	(794)1,205
1967	(25)306	(81)90	(660) 667	(766)1,063

Source: Consumer and Marketing Service, USDA.

Acreage allotments for a production year are announced the previous December. The price support loan rate is announced the following August 1. For rice harvested in late June and during July, there is no support price available. Consequently, rice harvested early must be stored until after August 1 or sold in an inactive market. The trend toward an earlier and shorter harvest season will continue to accentuate this problem.

There can be little doubt that the price support loan rate has a significant influence on the average market price. Table 8-9 shows the national average support rate and the season average support rate received by farmers. Between 1955, when acreage allotments began, and 1965, prices received by farmers exceeded the support rate by not more than 43.0 per hundredweight, with an average difference for the 1955-65 period of 27.7 cents. From 1961 through 1964, when the support rate held steady at $4.71, the margin dropped each year, going from $.43 in 1961 to $.19 in 1964.

Prices of some U. S. commodities are higher than "world" prices. To enable U. S. exporters to compete on even terms in world markets, export payments are made to U. S. exporters in amounts approximating the difference between the U. S. price and the world price. Export subsidies for rice from December 1958 to August 1966 were in the form of payments-in-kind from CCC stocks. In August 1966, the Department of Agriculture returned to a cash export payment for rice, wheat, flaxseed and linseed oil.

TABLE 8-9. RICE, ROUGH: NATIONAL AVERAGE SUPPORT RATE, SEASON AVERAGE PRICE RECEIVED BY FARMERS AND DIFFERENCE, 1948-65

Crop of	National average support rate per hundredweight	Season average price per hundredweight received by farmers	Difference
	— — — — — — Dollars — — — — — — —		
1948	4.08	4.88	.80
1949	3.96	4.10	.14
1950	4.56	5.09	.53
1951	5.00	4.82	—.18
1952	5.04	5.87	.83
1953	4.84	5.19	.35
1954	4.92	4.57	—.35
1955	4.66	4.81	.15
1956	4.57	4.86	.29
1957	4.72	5.11	.39
1958	4.48	4.68	.20
1959	4.38	4.59	.21
1960	4.42	4.55	.13
1961	4.71	5.14	.43
1962	4.71	5.04	.33
1963	4.71	5.01	.30
1964	4.71	4.90	.19
1965	4.50	4.93	.43

Source: *Rice Situation,* January 1967.

Export payment rates are announced weekly by the USDA for two groups of long-grain rice, medium-grain, Pearl and Calrose rice. For milled long-grain varieties of Patna, Bluebonnet, Rexoro, Belle Patna, Rexark and Vegold the subsidy rate per hundredweight by selected dates was: November 1, 1965—$2.51; February 7, 1966—$2.68; July 25, 1966—$1.18; December 13, 1966—$1.87; April 10, 1967—$.75; and May 8, 1967—$0.0. Since the last date mentioned, there has been no export subsidy on rice other than Pearl which is subsidized at the rate of 86 cents.

Probably the most relevant picture of the effects of government involvement in rice marketing can be seen by looking at the total supply-utilization relationship over time. Table 8-10 relates total supply at the beginning of the marketing year to domestic disappearance and both commercial and government exports. Domestic disappearance, in the 1960's, has trended steadily upward, as have commercial exports. Government program exports exhibit no such trend except for the large increase for 1966-67 and have apparently served to move the residual supply, thus operating in a market-clearing fashion. From the standpoint of the industry as a whole, one would have to conclude that government program exports have complemented rather than conflicted with industry objectives.

TABLE 8-10. RICE, ROUGH EQUIVALENT: TOTAL SUPPLY, DOMESTIC DISAPPEARANCE AND EXPORTS, 1959-66

Year beginning August	Total supply	Domestic disappearance	Exports[1]	
			Commercial	Government programs
— — — — — — — — 1,000 cwt. — — — — — — — —				
1959	70,106	27,750	11,015	18,218
1960	67,023	26,920	9,732	19,742
1961	64,663	29,591	16,006	13,149
1962	71,413	27,943	15,269	20,257
1963	78,016	28,767	22,348	19,455
1964	81,174	31,088	24,679	17,842
1965	84,638	30,846	26,219	17,096
1966	93,273	31,494	25,287	26,744

[1]Breakdown between commercial and government programs on basis of fiscal year.
Source: Economic Research Service, USDA.

CONCLUDING STATEMENT

The U. S. rice industry depends heavily on foreign market outlets. In 1966, for instance, exports accounted for over 60 percent of total utilization. The wars in Vietnam and the Middle East, famine in India and short crops of rice in Burma and Thailand have elevated the United States to the position of leading rice exporter.

U. S. farm programs are designed to maintain farm income and maintain a proper balance between the supply of and demand for farm products. It is to be expected—given the world conditions of recent years—that foreign policy objectives and domestic programs should conflict to a degree at times. With respect to rice there have been areas of complementarity and conflict. From the farm viewpoint, government programs have served to translate latent demand into effective demand, as export subsidies have expanded commercial markets and PL-480 exports have eliminated the surpluses of the mid-1950's and have held carryover at minimum levels. Farmer's current production has moved into export at prices averaging well above the domestic support level.

Conflicts have centered on the effect of timing of PL-480 procurements on the operation of individual firms, and probably the major conflicts arise because of a lack of understanding and communication between producers, processors and the involved government agencies. Domestic disappearance, in the 1960's, has trended steadily upward, as have commercial exports. From the standpoint of the industry as a whole, government program exports have apparently complemented rather than conflicted with industry objectives. At the same time, individuals may justifiably question certain operating procedures of the government export programs.

9

Market Organizational Potentials in the Rice Industry

Richard S. Berberich
Marshall R. Godwin
Ewell P. Roy

The rice industry over the past few decades has looked increasingly toward the Federal Government for aid and assistance in controlling production, stabilizing prices and exporting rice. In so doing, many alternative or complementary courses of action may not have received sufficient attention by the industry. Existing federal legislation provides a number of alternative approaches by which growers and other industry groups may attain a higher level of organization within the rice industry. However, there are constraints on the the extent to which such legislation can be used by this group to enhance prices or influence trade terms. In addition to action that may be taken under the aegis of federal statutes, the potentialities of developing unified marketing programs through state enabling legislation should be considered. Arkansas, Louisiana, Mississippi and Texas lag behind California in permissive state legislation that may be used by rice producers, as well as other producer groups.

There are several reasons why producers and others in the rice industry of the southern region, and especially in the three Gulf Coast rice producing states, may find it desirable or advantageous to escalate the level of organization by producers and of handling and marketing firms. The first of these pertains to the prospects of achieving a higher order of efficiency in the marketing process. Organizational effort that would result in increasing operational scale at a particular level in the marketing system or which may produce a higher capability to coordinate and control the continuum of functions extending forward from the production stage has prospects of efficiency gains for the industry. The experience with horizontal and vertical integration by producers in Arkansas and California provides considerable support for this contention. The ability to coordinate marketing processes and to exercise control over product flow into use channels offers further potential gains in the form of increased bargaining power for the rice industry. Given the scale of buying firms both in the domestic and export market, it appears that producers and firms operating at early stages in the marketing sequence may benefit from a level of organization which could provide them with more countervailing power in the market place. Again, this need appears to be less critical in Arkansas than for producers and local storage or marketing firms in Mississippi, Louisiana and Texas. Finally, it appears likely that the economic destiny of the rice industry will continue to be tied in some measure to the national and international programs of the federal government. Yet the comparatively small number of farmers and of firms involved in handling rice means that the industry, collectively, has a limited capability to influence national policy to its advantage or to the end of equity. This shortcoming can be overcome only if the industry is sufficiently well organized to present a unified approach on national policy questions which affect it.

All of these considerations suggest that the rice industry in the United States should examine rather carefully the means by which it may gain greater economic and political power. This is a matter which should especially command the attention of producers and marketing firms of the three-state region consisting of Texas, Louisiana and Mississippi, where the organizational integrity of the industry is less fully developed than elsewhere.

LEGISLATION ON MARKET ORGANIZATION

The more pertinent legislation on market organization includes the Sherman, Clayton, Federal Trade Commission and Robinson-Patman Acts. These laws are designed to insure free, open and fair competition and to prohibit any activities that are or could be contrary to such objectives as restraint-of-trade agreements, monopoly, price discrimination, tie-in sales, mergers and other unfair methods of market competition.

The Sherman Act prohibits specifically such activities as price fixing, boycotts, territorial division and attempts to monopolize.

The Clayton Act prohibits similar conduct in their incipient or formative stage. The most common areas subject to Clayton Act violations are price discrimination, mergers and tie-in sales arrangements.

The Federal Trade Commission Act provides the FTC with authority to enforce most provisions of the Clayton Act; Section 5 of the FTC Act, which is equivalent to provisions contained in the Sherman Act, and the Robinson-Patman price discrimination law, which has as its purpose the prevention of discrimination in price and other discriminatory practices injuriously affecting free competitive enterprise. However, various laws have been enacted to exempt in whole or in part certain business groups and farmers' associations from the aforementioned laws. These are discussed subsequently.

194

Federal Legislation

Federal legislation applicable to farmer cooperatives includes the Capper-Volstead Act, Agricultural Marketing Agreements Act and Cooperative Marketing Act.

Capper-Volstead Act of 1922

Capper-Volstead was enacted to permit groups of farmers to organize for conducting business cooperatively without this action in itself constituting a violation of antitrust law.

To meet the provisions of Capper-Volstead, farmers' cooperatives must be operated for the mutual benefit of the members thereof, as such producers, and conform to one or both of the following requirements, and in any case to the third:

(1) That no member of the association is allowed more than one vote because of the amount of stock or membership capital he may own therein, or, (2) that the association does not pay dividends on stock or membership capital in excess of 8 percent per annum and (3) that the association shall not deal in the products of nonmembers to an amount greater in value than such as are handled by it for members.

Capper-Volstead applies to both farmers' marketing and bargaining associations. However, Capper-Volstead does not charter farmer cooperatives nor does it apply to farmers' purchasing cooperatives. Its principal aim is to allow farmers to join together legally for collective marketing and/or bargaining with buyers of produce over prices, terms and conditions of sale without these actions themselves being in violation of federal antitrust law.

Federations of farmer cooperative locals are also made possible under Capper-Volstead under the same terms and conditions which apply to a local.

It is very important that rice marketing and bargaining associations organized by producers and conducting trade of an interstate nature conform to the provisions of Capper-Volstead to avoid prosecution for conspiracy under the Sherman and Clayton Acts.

Agricultural Marketing Agreements Act of 1937

The Agricultural Marketing Agreements Act of 1937, amended by the Agricultural Act of 1961, provides for self-help programs which are designed to establish and maintain orderly market conditions for commodities moving in or affecting interstate or foreign commerce, at fair prices to the consumer and with equitable returns to the producer and handler. Their purpose is to give to the farmer some of the marketing advantages long enjoyed by industry.

The programs differ from other agricultural adjustment measures in that they combine voluntary and regulatory control—initiated, set up and directed by the industry. Each industry bears the costs of administering the program. The programs also demand aggressive group participation in their operation and development, with resultant interest and emphasis placed upon furthering agricultural private enterprise.

Thus far, *rice* is not an eligible commodity under the Act. There are increasing possibilities, however, for extending coverage of marketing orders to rice and other presently ineligible commodities. It appears that sentiment among growers and some industry leaders points to intensified efforts in the future toward including all farm commodities on the eligibility list for marketing orders. A marketing order for rice is discussed later in this report in connection with rice-producer bargaining efforts.

Cooperative Marketing Act of 1926

This Act exempts from antitrust the acquisition and exchange of past, present and prospective crop, statistical production and marketing data by farmers' cooperatives or their common agents.

State Legislation

Existing Laws for Farmer Cooperatives

The main rice-producing states of Arkansas, California, Louisiana, Mississippi and Texas have adequate legislation regarding farmer cooperatives and federations of them. California's farmer co-op laws are more elaborate and sophisticated than those in the other four states. For example, California law permits decision in farmer co-ops on bases other than one-man, one-vote, whereas legislation in Arkansas, Louisiana and Texas provides only for one-man, one-vote. Mississippi legislation provides for voting according to stock shares in certain specific situations in addition to the one-man, one-vote basis for control.[1] It is likely that the one-man, one-vote principle for cooperation may tend to hinder the organization of large rice producers into farmers' cooperatives. That is, a large rice producer has some cause for concern that he may be out-voted by smaller producers despite the fact that he may be contributing a large share of the rice handled by the cooperative. If voting were conducted on the basis of rice volume, more equitable decision-making might result as between large and small growers. The exact role which the one-man, one-vote principle plays in leading to or preventing rice co-op organization has not been established and is offered here as a hypothesis for research and evaluation.[2]

---

[1]Roy, E. P., *Cooperatives: Today and Tomorrow,* Interstate Printers and Publishers, Inc., Danville, Ill., 1964. pp. 253-281.

[2]Roy, E. P., "Do Cooperative Principles Need Reappraisal?" *Louisiana Rural Economist,* Vol. 29, No. 2, May 1967. pp. 2-5.

With regard to *state marketing orders,* only California, of the five main rice producing states, has extensive legislation permitting the organization and operation of state marketing orders although *rice* is not one of the commodities presently involved in California programs. It is permissible, however, for California rice farmers to petition for a state marketing order.[3,4,5]

In addition, California alone of the five states cited has recently adopted legislation which makes it illegal for anyone to interfere with a farmer's right to join a farmer cooperative or to discriminate against farmers who do join.

California legislation makes it unlawful for any processor, handler, distributor or his agent to:

1. Interfere with, restrain, coerce or boycott farmers who want to join bargaining associations.

2. Discriminate against farmers on price or other terms of buying farm products because they belong to co-op bargaining associations.

3. Pay or loan money to farmers to lure them out of bargaining associations.

4. Maliciously or knowingly give false reports about the finances, management or activities of a bargaining association.

Violations are misdemeanors punishable by a fine of not less than $50 nor more than $500.

Potential State Legislation

It is apparent that California has a more elaborate and comprehensive set of legislative tools for farmer cooperative marketing and bargaining than exists in the other four main rice producing states of Arkansas, Louisiana, Mississippi and Texas. Farmers in the latter four states might give consideration to California's legislation in an effort to adopt or adapt all or part of such legislation for their states.

Federal Legislation for Other Cooperative Organizations

The Webb-Pomerene Act

The Webb-Pomerene Act was passed in 1918 and is administered through the Federal Trade Commission. This law specifically permits

[3]Foytik, Jerry, *California Agricultural Marketing Orders,* California Agricultural Experiment Station Report 259, Berkeley, California, November 1962.

[4]Hoos, Sidney, *California Agricultural Marketing Programs,* California Agricultural Experiment Station Report 200, Berkeley, California, October 1957.

[5]Hoos, Sidney, *Economic Objectives and Operations of California Agricultural Marketing Orders,* California Agricultural Experiment Station Report 196, Berkeley, California, May 1957.

combinations in export trade and grants exemption from antitrust laws for that purpose. Webb-Pomerene associations may be made up of both profit and nonprofit type businesses.[6]

The Act was passed in order to legalize the formation of "cartel-like" groups which could compete with price fixing combines abroad which were monopolizing the world export market. Many single producers do not have adequate size, volume and power to compete in foreign markets; hence, the Webb-Pomerene Act was passed in order to insure profitable export prices and to promote cooperation legally among U. S. producers. Through successful cooperative organizations, producers and marketers can share the costs of developing new markets, establish themselves firmly in foreign markets, extend credit more readily to foreign customers and compete more successfully with foreign cartels.

The law was specifically intended to settle once and for all time the doubt as to the application of antitrust laws to cooperative export organizations.

The first of five organizational steps outlined by the Act is to assemble participants of the industry to establish common objectives concerning developing and maintaining export trade.

A second step would be to attend to details such as (a) incorporation; (b) dividend policy; (c) voting policy and (d) countries to trade with, among many other such organizational details.

A third step would include a list of functions to be adopted by the export associations including standardizing products for export and improving the quality of the goods; maintaining inspection services, employing claims agents and settling disputes over export sales; establishing rules and regulations for packing and shipping the goods; arranging for freight rates, cargo space and shipping dates; consolidating the shipments of the members; taking out insurance and such.

The fourth step would involve a conference with the Federal Trade Commission prior to completion of organizational forms.

The fifth step would include making periodic reports to the FTC of the activities of the export group and of such other details as the FTC might require.

Export groups are scrutinized closely by the FTC to determine whether their export activities are utilized as a cover for collusion in the domestic market.

[6]Beer, H. W., *Federal Trade Law and Practices*, Baker, Voorhis & Co., Inc., New York, N. Y. 1942. pp. 544-555.

Webb-Pomerene associations for rice presently in existence export about $21 million worth of rice out of total rice exports of $152.6 million or 13.8 percent of total exports.[7]

It appears that rice as an export product meets the following specifications outlined by the Federal Trade Commission for successful Webb-Pomerene Associations: (1) a standardized product, (2) concentration of production among a few firms and (3) the existence of a comparative trade advantage in the manufacture and sale of the product.

Small Business Act

Under the Small Business Act, nonfarm business cooperatives are allowed to qualify for loans from the Small Business Administration. Such loans are intended to enable small business concerns to jointly finance plant construction, conversion or expansion facilities, machinery, supplies or other materials. Loans are also provided for working capital.

Another provision of the Small Business Act provides for funds to small business cooperatives to conduct joint research and development activities.[8]

These two programs if used more extensively in the nonfarm rice industry could lead to improvements in the rice drying, storage and milling phases by modernizing facilities, upgrading technology and economically preserving smaller firms which otherwise may not survive.

Federal Chartering Statutes

Nonfarm business cooperatives have no protection in organization as do farmer cooperatives under Capper-Volstead. There are no federal incorporation statutes for nonfarm business cooperatives. The latter must charter under respective state laws and conform to antitrust law, either or both state and federal, in the conduct of their business.

Existing State Laws for Nonfarm Business Cooperatives

While a detailed review of state laws regarding the organization of nonfarm business cooperatives in the five main rice producing states was not conducted, more general information indicates that in Arkansas, California and Louisiana, incorporating statutes, designed specifically for nonfarm business cooperatives, are available. Mississippi and Texas, while having no such specific statutes, would likely

[7]Mueller, W. F., *Nature and Scope of Webb-Pomerene Associations*, Judiciary Committee, U. S. Senate, Washington, D. C., June 26, 1967, Appendix Table 5.

[8]Hack, Stanley, *Legal Aspects of Small Businesses' Use of Cooperative Arrangements*, University of Wisconsin, Madison, Wisconsin, December 1964. pp. 77-80.

accommodate nonfarm business cooperatives under their general corporation law.[9]

The purposes of nonfarm business cooperatives organized by profit-type drier, miller and other rice agribusinesses may be enumerated as follows:

1. To purchase manufacturing and other business equipment and supplies cooperatively, other than rough rice, within antitrust law.

2. To coordinate, consolidate and pool freight, transportation and warehousing operations cooperatively within antitrust law.

3. To collect and disseminate trade and other data cooperatively but excluding price, costs and margins data.

4. To provide business services cooperatively such as quality control, advertising, sales promotion, joint brands, merchandising assistances and improved marketing techniques, within the scope of antitrust law.

5. To form joint sales agencies for the marketing of milled rice to food manufacturers, cereal makers, breweries, food wholesalers and retailers, within the scope of antitrust law. Particular attention would need to be given to the nature and type of joint sales agency to determine more precisely its validity and sanction under federal antitrust law.

It should be noted that nonfarm business cooperatives do not have the same type or degree of immunity from antitrust law as is provided farmers' cooperatives under the Capper-Volstead, Agricultural Marketing Agreements Act and Cooperative Marketing Act. Nevertheless, there are many areas of business activity which may be conducted jointly within the scope of antitrust law.

By operating cooperatively in certain legally permissible operations, it is likely that smaller rice agribusinesses could reduce unit costs by achieving greater economies to scale and strengthen their competitive position relative to the larger firms in the rice business. The potentials offered here would appear worthy of further investigation. However, cooperative organization among nonfarm rice agribusinesses would have to meet more rigorous antitrust examination than for comparable rice producer organizations.[10] Some of these possible legal constraints are discussed later in this report.

Legislative Constraints on Cooperatives

Farmer cooperatives are subject to the Sherman, Clayton, Federal Trade Commission, Robinson-Patman, Wheeler-Lea and other Acts

[9]Roy, Cooperatives: Today and Tomorrow, *op. cit.,* pp. 256-257.
[10]Hack, *op. cit.,* pp. 240-258.

designed to restrain monopoly or monopoly-producing tactics and to promote more effective competition.

Legislative constraints on farmer cooperatives are discussed in terms of enforcement procedures of the U. S. Department of Justice and the FTC.

U. S. Department of Justice Position on Farmer Cooperatives Based on Sherman and Clayton Acts

Donald F. Turner, assistant attorney general, U. S. Department of Justice, has expressed that department's position on farmer cooperatives as follows:

> Were I forced to summarize, and thus probably over-simplify, the effect of these and related statutes (Sherman Act, Clayton Act and Capper-Volstead) upon the exemption for agricultural cooperatives, I should say that they have led to the formulation of two general rules. First, farmers and producers may form cooperatives without violating the antitrust laws, but once formed, cooperatives should by and large be treated like other businesses under the antitrust laws. Second, membership in cooperatives must remain voluntary.
>
> The fact that cooperatives, as a general rule, are to be treated like other businesses is shown by the history of the Clayton and Capper-Volstead Acts and by the decisions of the courts interpreting the cooperative exemption.[11]

Court cases in the matter of farmer cooperatives thus far have established the following salient points:

1. Farmer cooperatives may legally attain monopoly status provided this is accomplished voluntarily without discrimination and restraint and provided prices are not unduly enhanced, as language of the Capper-Volstead Act specifies.

2. Farmer cooperatives must not combine or conspire with non-cooperatives to fix prices.[12]

3. Farmer cooperatives must not engage in predatory conduct and must not substantially lessen competition when it acquires a competitor firm.[13]

4. The Capper-Volstead Act specifically states that cooperatives may have marketing agencies in common. Presumably, therefore, two or more cooperatives in a particular area would not be precluded from joining together to create a single marketing agency merely by

---

[11]Turner, Donald F., "Cooperatives and Antitrust," *Proceedings of National Conference of Fruit and Vegetable Bargaining Cooperatives,* FCS, USDA, Washington, D. C., January 17, 1966.

[12]U. S. versus *Borden Company,* 308 U. S. 188 (1939).

[13]*Maryland and Virginia Milk Producers Association* versus *U. S.,* 362 U. S. 458 (1960).

the fact that they had marketed or could market in competition with each other. In contrast, the formation of a common marketing agency by a competing group of, say, steel manufacturers would almost certainly be illegal.[14]

5. Farmer cooperatives must not coerce outsiders by secondary boycott or blacklisting.[15]

6. Farmer cooperatives may form intra-enterprises or federated marketing agencies within the purview of the Clayton and Capper-Volstead Acts.[16]

7. Farmer cooperatives under Capper-Volstead may not have non-farmers or associations of nonfarmers as members according to a recent Supreme Court decision.[17]

Role of Federal Trade Commission in Relation to Cooperatives

At least three salient cases have come before the FTC regarding co-op operations:

1. Purchasing cooperatives may not combine to obtain illegally discriminatory prices and to obtain other preferential treatment from suppliers not available to their competitors.[18]

2. Marketing cooperatives may not conspire and utilize coercive tactics to ensure that they will supply all the market requirements of certain processors or buyers and may not discriminate in price between purchasers of commodities in competition with each other.[19]

3. Section 4 of the Robinson-Patman Act, the legislative statement encouraging cooperatives in this area, provides that nothing in the Act is to be construed as preventing a cooperative from returning the whole or part of its net earnings or surplus to its members, producers or consumers in proportion to their purchases or sales from, to or through the organization.[20]

Other important constraints on business activity and market competition imposed by the FTC include prohibitions against false advertising, secret rebates to customers, below-cost selling to destroy competitors, threatening of customers, long-term exclusive dealing contracts, territorial price discrimination to eliminate competitors and ganging-up on troublesome competitors.

---

[14]Turner, *op. cit.*, pp. 5-6.

[15]*U. S.* versus *King,* 229 Fed. 275; 250 Fed. 908.

[16]*Sunkist Growers* versus *Winckler and Smith Citrus Products Company,* 370 U. S. 19 (1962).

[17]*Case-Swayne Co.* versus *Sunkist Growers.* Dec. 18,1967.

[18]*Atlas Supply Company,* 48 FTC 53 (1951).

[19]*Central Arkansas Milk Producers Association,* FTC Docket 8391 (1964).

[20]49 Stat. 1528 (1936), 15 U. S. C., paragraph 13 (b) (1958).

The FTC's general position on cooperatives has been heretofore quite strict and scrutinizing. More recently, the FTC has adopted a posture of relaxing restraints somewhat in the case of farmers' cooperatives and small business cooperatives where their group existence would *add to* rather than *subtract from* market competition.

Commissioner Everette Macintyre has stated the FTC's more recent attitudes as follows:

> With the exception of hard core violations involving predatory practices, in the case of small business or farmers' cooperatives, it may be expected that the Commission will increasingly look at the economic and competitive function of the particular cooperative and where permissible, will apply the rule of reason.[21]

CURRENT LEVEL OF MARKET ORGANIZATION IN THE RICE INDUSTRY

This section examines the current status of cooperative development in the major rice producing areas. It includes a brief description of the operations of three major cooperatives and an examination of the two organizations in the rice industry whose operations are national in scope.

Status of Cooperatives

Cooperatives are an important part of the U.S. rice industry. In 1967, 65 rice cooperatives operated in the United States. Of these, 57 were local cooperative driers, 6 warehoused and milled rice and 2 provided certain marketing functions for members. Six were in California, 20 in Arkansas, 18 each in Louisiana and Texas and 3 in Mississippi (Table 9-1).

A wide variation exists in the percentage of rice handled by cooperatives in major producing states. In California, cooperatives market over 80 percent of the rice, although only one-fourth of the rough rice is cooperatively dried. Cooperatives handle over 60 percent of the total drying, storing and marketing of rice in Arkansas.

---

[21]Macintyre, Everette, "Cooperatives," *American Bar Association Proceedings,* New York, N. Y. August 11, 1964. pp. 10-11.

TABLE 9-1. RICE COOPERATIVES IN THE U.S., 1966-67

State	Milling	Local driers	Other	Total
California	2	4		6
Arkansas	2	18		20
Texas	1	17		18
Louisiana	1	16	1	18
Mississippi		2	1	3
Total	6	57	2	65

In Louisiana and Texas cooperatives dry and store over 40 percent of the rice produced, but they mill only around 15 percent.

The average plant capacity of cooperative mills is large in comparison with the industry average. Cooperatives have an average daily capacity of approximately 18,000 barrels a day while the average for all mills is around 7,000.

Rice growers in California and Arkansas have integrated processing and marketing through the cooperatives that currently handle the major part of the rice in these states.

In Louisiana, Texas and Mississippi, cooperatives are less integrated in operations and services to growers. Here farmer cooperatives primarily dry and store rice. There is no effective tie between the cooperative mills and cooperative driers in these states. Sales of rough rice generally are conducted in bid-type markets where prospective buyers inspect rice samples and submit sealed bids on specified lots. Cooperative mills along with all other commercial mills bid competitively on rice.

Types of Cooperative Rice Organizations and Services Performed

Types of rice cooperatives include regionals, branches of centralized regionals, locals affiliated with federated regionals and independent locals. The activities of these cooperatives range from performing a single function in the marketing process to performing a complete job of drying, storing, milling and selling rice. Other services include handling seed rice and farm supplies and, to a limited extent, operating irrigation facilities. Cooperative marketing associations also perform merchandising and sales promotion services for their members.

Organizational Structure and Operations of Three Large Rice Cooperatives

The Arkansas and California experiences have shown that cooperatives can successfully integrate their operations from production through processing and selling. The operation of integrated cooperatives in Arkansas and California and of cooperatives in the Gulf area is described in the following sections.

Arkansas Rice Growers Cooperative Association

This association at Stuttgart is an example of an integrated operation under centralized control. This association was organized in 1920 as a rough rice marketing cooperative. In 1926 the association purchased a rice mill and since that time has marketed practically all of its members' production in the form of milled rice.

Facilities

The Arkansas Rice Growers Cooperative Association operates four mills—one at Jonesboro and three at Stuttgart. One of the mills at Stuttgart is especially designed for parboiled rice. The association also has storage and shipping facilities and a modern packaging plant.

The first local drier affiliate was organized in 1944. Now there are 18 local drying and storing cooperatives affiliated with Arkansas Rice Growers Cooperative. The rapid acceptance of the combine method of harvesting rice in Arkansas in the early 1940's resulted in establishing these drying and storage facilities in the producing areas.

The Arkansas Grain Corporation, an affiliate cooperative, was organized in 1958 to process and market soybeans and small grains. This cooperative has two soybean processing plants and a third one authorized in 1968 for Stuttgart. All plants are equipped with degumming, refining and deodorizing facilities. All plants produce salad oil or cooking oil in a continuous operation. In addition a salad oil canning plant at New Orleans was recently activated with a capacity of 60 gallons per minute.

All storage facilities, locals as well as at the mills, are constructed of concrete. They are equipped with extremely high capacity receiving, drying, handling and load-out machinery. The facilities have been modernized to keep pace with the technological changes in harvesting on the farm and in transportation equipment.

Directors and Officers

The business affairs of the Arkansas Rice Growers Association are conducted by a board of directors elected by the members, including one from each location of the 18 affiliated driers. It is the responsibility of the board to establish policies and employ management. The manager supervises the association's entire operation including the subsidiary drier cooperatives and the Riceland Sales Company which is the cooperative's marketing agency.

Operations of the Corporate Complex

The affiliation of the Arkansas Rice Growers Cooperative Association in the corporate complex includes the Arkansas Grain Corporation and eighteen grain drying cooperatives. Arkansas rice growers have a duel membership in their cooperative: one with their local grain drying cooperative and the other with the Arkansas Rice Growers Cooperative.

Farmers in the community own local driers and also own a share of the processing facilities and market organization in the central cooperative at Stuttgart. The operation provides for local ownership of facilities and for centralized control of marketing and processing functions. The responsibility of the local is to receive, grade, dry, condition and store rice delivered by the members. The Arkansas Rice Growers Association pays service fees to the local for these functions. The local maintains the rice in storage until delivery is called for by Arkansas Rice Association. The title to the rice thus passes from the grower to the marketing organization (Arkansas Rice Growers Cooperative), and the rice goes into a pool. The local makes the initial advance to the grower upon delivery of the rice. All subsequent payments to growers are made by the Arkansas Rice Association directly from headquarters in Stuttgart. Each check is accompanied by a statement showing volume delivered by variety, grade, milling quality and yield.

The Arkansas Grain Corporation operates in the same manner as the Arkansas Rice Growers Cooperative and has the same top management. Both rice and soybeans have been integrated into the overall complex. The soybean and rice facilities are on the same property which results in better utilization of labor including administrative staff. Also, since rice is harvested before soybeans, the soybean elevators can be used to receive, condition and store rice until the soybean harvest starts.

The Arkansas Rice Growers Cooperative Association, with a membership of over 5,000 rice growers, handled approximately 427,000 tons of rice in the 1965-66 season. Over 60 percent of the association's rice sales were exported with the balance to domestic markets.

Economic Contributions of Association

One measure of success for a marketing cooperative is the percentage of sales revenue returned to its members. The Arkansas Rice Growers Cooperative Association has averaged returns of 88 percent of its gross sales to its members. The remaining 12 percent represents the costs of processing and marketing. The affliate cooperative, Arkansas Grain, has returned an average of 90 percent of the gross sales to its members during 8 complete years of operation. Since most of the soybean products are shipped in bulk, the cost of processing and marketing is somewhat less for soybeans than for rice.

Rice Growers Association of California

Another example of cooperative integration is the Rice Growers Association of California. This association, with headquarters at Sacramento, began operations as a rice-bargaining cooperative but soon expanded its functions into milling and marketing to gain the market strength needed to obtain improved returns for member growers. This cooperative is a centralized organization. This facilitates decision-making for both milling and sales operations. Its membership has grown at a steady pace.

The association was organized in 1921 and incorporated under the Agricultural Code of the State of California. It handled rough rice only from 1921 until 1925 and functioned primarily as a bargaining cooperative. As the association was not too successful in obtaining better prices for the growers in this rather limited role, it expanded its rice operations into milling and sales of the finished product under centralized control.

The Rice Growers Association currently handles more than 60 percent of the State's rice crop.

Facilities

The association owns and operates two mills in West Sacramento, one in Biggs, and one in Woodland, California, with a combined capacity of 50,000 hundredweight of rough rice per day. It also has eight rice driers with locations at West Sacramento (4 driers), Biggs, Merritt, Willows and Woodland, and storage facilities connected with each drier. Approximately 3 million hundredweight of rough rice from the 1966 crop were dried in these facilities and about 3.3 million hundredweight were stored.

Other operating facilities owned by the association include an oil extraction plant in West Sacramento and a packaging plant at San Juan, Puerto Rico.

Management and Staff

The association's affairs are managed and controlled by a board of 25 directors, each of whom must be a member of the association and can hold office for 1 year.

An executive committee made up of eight members of the board functions between sessions of the board.

The president of the association is also the general manager and he supervises the overall operations.

The association has 68 employees in its administrative setup including executive management, production supervision, field and grower relationship, sales and traffic, accounting and general office work. In addition, it has about 250 production employees on a semi-permanent basis.

Method of Paying Members

The Rice Growers Association handles all rice on a dry basis for settlement to growers. Although the association processes and markets all of its members' rice, the members do have a choice of using the association's drying facilities or any other on-farm, commercial or cooperative drier. When a grower delivers his rice to one of the association's mills, the association makes a cash advance to the grower consistent with the market conditions and places the rice in a pool. It makes further advances to the grower at specified dates throughout the year.

The total amount of the member's rice is converted to a money equivalent and the net proceeds are distributed to the growers on the basis of No. 1 quality rice. Growers failing to meet the No. 1 standard for their rice are assessed a damage penalty in cash to raise their rice to a price equivalent to No. 1 quality.

Table 9-2 illustrates the method used for deriving the proceeds to growers per 100 pounds of dried rice delivered to the mill.

Operational Cost Per Hundredweight

The Rice Growers Association estimates the cost to the grower on a dry weight basis per hundredweight of rough rice. The grower initially assumes the responsibility for drying his rice which should average about 25 cents per hundredweight. The total cost that R.G.A. charges its members averages about $1 per hundredweight of rough rice. Included in this cost would be 15 cents for freight into the mill, 20 cents for storage, with the balance of the cost including milling the rice, general administrative expenses, financing charges, dividends, brokerage and personal property tax.

Grading

The cooperative has developed its own system for grading rice delivered by its members with grades comparable to the government's grading structure.

Promotion

The major part of the co-op's promotional activities are in the Puerto Rican market. The programs include newspaper, radio and television advertising, as well as award winning contests for consumers. Other areas that have responded well to promotional programs include Hawaii and New York City.

TABLE 9-2. EXAMPLE OF AVERAGE NET RETURN PER HUNDRED-WEIGHT TO GROWERS FOR RICE HANDLED BY RGA

Rice milling yields	Assumed price	Gross return per 100 pounds	Net return to growers per 100 pounds[1]
Head rice — 50 percent	$9.00 per cwt.	$4.50 (50 lb.)	$3.60 (50 lb.)
Broken rice — 20 percent	6.00 per cwt.	1.20 (20 lb.)	.96 (20 lb.)
By-products — 10 percent	2.00 per cwt.	.20 (10 lb.)	.16 (10 lb.)
Hulls and waste — 20 percent	0	0 (20 lb.)	0 (20 lb.)
Total		$5.90 (100 lb.)	$4.72 (100 lb.)

[1]Estimated 20 percent deduction for total expenses.

Selling Methods

R.G.A.'s rice sales are mainly handled through brokers. However, direct sales are made to cereal manufacturers in the domestic market and to a large extent in exports to Japan and Okinawa.

The association's centralized sales program has shown results in all important world markets. However, the main effort is concentrated in those markets which have the best long-range sales potential—the continental U. S., Puerto Rico, Hawaii, Okinawa, Guam and Japan.

Markets Served

The important domestic markets of R.G.A. for consumer trade of whole rice include New York City and the West Coast. In addition, large quantities of whole and broken rice are sold to cereal manufacturers, and broken rice is sold to breweries.

The Rice Growers Association has developed a large market in Puerto Rico for its table rice. R.G.A.'s sales to Puerto Rico under the Red Seal brand equal its total domestic sales of whole grain, broken rice and rice products. Bulk handling and shipping rice to the association's packaging plant in Puerto Rico have aided in market development.

Other important markets outside the continental U. S. include Japan, Okinawa and Hawaii. A major development in the export sales program for the past crop year has been the large rice sales to Korea and Vietnam.

Economic Contributions of Association

The association has consistently given its members as high or higher returns than any other group in the California rice industry. In the 1964-65 and 1965-66 seasons the average net return to rice growers has been $4.92 and $4.87 per hundredweight, respectively, which approximated 83 and 86 cents per hundredweight above the net support price.[22]

The California rice industry under the leadership of the Rice Growers Association has made a significant breakthrough in establishing an effective export sales program under the control of the California Rice Export Corporation. Recognizing the need for a stabilized price on export sales from California, the Rice Growers Association, together with Farmers Rice Cooperative in San Francisco and the two largest commercial mills in California, formed the California Rice Export Corporation. These four organizations handle over 90 percent of the total rice production in California. Consequently, the export corporation can influence price and quantity of California rice for export to important dollar markets such as Japan, Korea and Okinawa.

[22]1965 and 1966 Annual Reports of Rice Growers Association of California.

American Rice Growers Cooperative Association

The American Rice Growers Cooperative Association, organized in 1921, is a federation of 19 local rice cooperatives in Louisiana and Texas with a central office at Lake Charles, Louisiana.

The business of the association is under the direction of a board of directors representing local member associations who are elected at the annual meeting and serve a 1-year term.

The cooperative maintains contacts with various groups in the rice industry; helps develop and expand market outlets for rice; cooperates with federal and state agencies on rice programs; and keeps local managers and members informed on sales information, stock position, market conditions, prices and related data both in this country and abroad. It provides farm supply services and book-keeping services for cooperative dryers. Also, the central office supervises two rough rice grading offices, one located at Beaumont and the other at Eagle Lake, Texas.

Operation of Member Associations

The operations of the American Rice Growers Cooperative Association are carried on through 19 member locals, 9 in Louisiana and 10 in Texas. Each local operates as a separate entity in its drying, storage and sales functions for rough rice. Each local has its own officers and directors and retains possession of revenues accruing from its operations.

The 19 member locals of the association own and operate facilities for receiving, handling, drying and storing rough rice in bulk or bags. One of the locals also owns an irrigation system to supply its members with water for rice production.

Each member's rough rice is delivered to the local and weighed upon arrival at the warehouse. Samples of the rice are taken for the association's grader and the warehouse manager issues a receipt to the grower-member covering such rice. Confidential grade information is furnished to the member as soon as the samples have been tested in the association's grading office. The member then determines when his rice shall be sold, based on the grader's certificate plus additional information from the local on sales of comparable grades of rice in various markets.

Sales offices are maintained at the local's headquarters with sales rooms provided for rough rice buyers. The method for handling sales at the local offices is for the local manager to announce dates for the sales and to display samples of rough rice in the sales room. Sales are held at least once a week during the marketing season with each lot of rice sold to the highest bidder within the price limitation specified by the producer.

The member locals of the American Rice Growers Cooperative Association handled a total sales volume of 14.2 million hundredweight of rough rice at a total dollar value of $70.6 million for the year ending June 30, 1966.

An affiliated cooperative, the American Grain Association organized in 1965, markets soybeans. It has the same general management as American Rice Growers Cooperative Association.

In the 1966-67 season this association handled soybeans with sales value of over $1 million for approximately 250 members.

Promotional and Trade Associations for Rice

The U. S. rice industry has made considerable progress in developing product demand in the domestic and export markets through promotion by advertising, publicity and education. The industry, however, has been relatively ineffective in unifying its position on economic and political matters.

The two leading organizations engaged in advancing and promoting the rice industry are the Rice Millers Association and the Rice Council.[23] Most of their accomplishments have been in promotional and educational activities. The Rice Millers Association has also been active in political and economic matters.

Rice Millers Association

The Rice Millers Association (R.M.A.) is a nonstock, nonprofit trade association of the rice milling industry. The association was organized in 1899 and includes a large membership of commercial rice mills in the U. S., both cooperative and profit-type.

The functions of R.M.A. include collecting and analyzing economic and statistical information on production, milling and distributing rice; acting as a liaison agency between the rice milling industry and legislators, departments of government, producers and handlers of rice; maintaining offices in important markets to gather market information and promoting favorable relations between member firms and traders in the respective markets; and providing members with requested information dealing with the economics of the rice industry.

The Rice Council

The Rice Council, a nonprofit organization formed in 1959, promotes the use of rice and rice products through advertising, publicity and education. It is supported by all segments of the rice industry in Arkansas, Louisiana, Mississippi and Texas.

---

[23]The American Rice Growers Association also engages in this type of activity as a part of its total operations as pointed out earlier.

The Council carries on an intensive marketing and promotional campaign and is recognized as the promotional voice of the industry. It provides a coordinated plan for keeping rice in the public view. The campaign includes national consumer advertising, special market promotions through newspapers, radio and television, publicity through food editors, dissemination of recipe books on rice and financial support of the U. S. Rice Export Development Association for promotional efforts to increase use of U. S. rice abroad. The Council carries on promotional programs abroad through offices and test kitchens in Zurich, London, Copenhagen, Brussels, Frankfort/Main and Pretoria. The Council programs the local needs in these countries through trained and qualified country representatives.

POTENTIALS FOR FURTHER ORGANIZATION

Rice producers may integrate their marketing activities horizontally and vertically by organizing cooperatives which physically handle the product. They may bargain over prices, terms and conditions without physical handling. Or they may do some of both.

Farmers may also organize profit-type corporations as investor-stockholders and patrons. However, discussion in this section is limited primarily to cooperative and industrywide types of arrangements.

Interest in various types of farmer cooperatives in the United States is increasing for several reasons:

1. The slow but constant expansion of contract farming into many crop and livestock enterprises. Farmers or contractees who produce these products see a need for improving their bargaining power relative to contractors. Also, food processors and retailers are becoming more specific in their buying requirements on quantity, quality and timing of deliveries.[24]

2. The market power of labor unions, agricultural middlemen and food retailers is increasing. This is coming about through larger size, market coordination, direct buying, mass distribution, further processing, development of convenience foods, product specifications, product branding, private labels, precision merchandising and regularity and guaranty of supply.

3. Accelerated growth of agribusiness firms capable of developing a policy of administered-prices and of labor unions for administered-wages. Mergers and consolidations continue to fuel this capability.

4. The growing complexity of the agricultural supply and marketing system. Farmers feel more helpless as individuals to cope with this complexity.

---

[24]Roy, E. P., Contract Farming, USA, Interstate Printers and Publishers, Inc., Danville, Ill. 1963. Chapter 1.

5. Deterioration in the traditional free, open, auction markets and their replacement by direct marketing with negotiated, formula-type prices and markets.

6. Loss of farmers' political power in state legislatures and in the Congress and farmers' lack of understanding and use of more complex government programs such as marketing orders.

7. The rather unfavorable plight of young farmers heavily in debt and facing high land costs, machinery investment, and the like, coupled with rising family demands on their farm income.

8. Increasing horizontal and vertical integration in the food business with retailers taking over the wholesaler functions (vertical) and retailers buying out other retailers (horizontal).

9. Improved internal operations in food business firms: increased use of computers, automated production lines and mechanized handling of inventory.

10. Increased unit costs of supplies used by farmers and higher unit labor costs because of higher minimum wage laws.

11. Increased specialization on the farm itself. A farmer specializing in one crop or enterprise is more seriously concerned about that enterprise than if he were diversified by having several enterprises.

COOPERATIVE MARKETING AND HANDLING ASSOCIATIONS

The rice industry in the Gulf area has the required characteristics for cooperative development in integrating drying, storing, milling and selling functions.

Rice production is concentrated in localized areas on relatively large farms. It is thus well suited to uniform assembly and large volume handling.

The Gulf area of Louisiana and Texas includes a large number of relatively small drying and milling firms. Many mills lack size to realize economies of scale in processing and necessary volume to bargain effectively with large buyers in our current market structure.

The present system of drying and storing rice maintains ownership identity on practically every lot of rice, which leads to poorly utilized storage. Commingling lots of rice of like quality and variety for sale by cooperatives without regard to ownership could reduce costs and increase income of growers.

Sales of rough rice by cooperatives and others are generally conducted in bid-type markets in which prospective buyers inspect the rice samples and submit sealed bids for specified lots. At a given time these bids are opened and each lot of rice is sold to the highest bidder, provided the price is within limits specified by the producer. Frequently growers with rice for sale are present at the time bids are opened.

The cooperative mills in the Gulf area (one each in Louisiana and Texas) competitively bid on rice samples along with other commercial mills. Consequently, there is no real tie between the cooperative mills and cooperative driers.

In contrast, the majority of Arkansas and California producers pool their rice through cooperatives. Pooling enables a cooperative to assemble the rice in significant quantities and of the quality needed to attract buyers in the best markets. Pooling also gives the cooperative more flexibility in obtaining government price support on their members' rice.

Once rice is delivered to a cooperative drier in Arkansas and California it remains under the control of the members' cooperative until it reaches wholesaler or retailer. Thus, members of these cooperatives have an opportunity to share in margins earned at various stages of handling and marketing.

The successful operating experiences of large integrated rice cooperatives in Arkansas and California indicate that the growers' best possibility for maximum returns is through broadening their operational base to include cooperative processing and marketing. This gives the growers an opportunity to venture into middle marketing and share in possible proceeds beyond the value of their harvested crop.

Growers in the Gulf area of Louisiana and Texas should consider establishing a marketing system which integrates the operations of drying, storing, milling and selling rice. Thought should also be given to adding one or more complementary crops, such as soybeans, to the rice operation.

Growers should consider the feasibility of acquiring some well-established drying and milling firms and operating them on a cooperative basis. In this way, they would have the opportunity of retaining the professional management of the acquired companies and thereby have an established team working for them with experience in processing and marketing.

The acquisition route permits growers to integrate both vertically and horizontally and achieve market strength to compete on more equal terms with buyers. It also gives them an opportunity to share in proceeds from further handling and processing.

214

More and more of the rice areas in Louisiana and Texas are shifting to a soybean-rice rotation rather than rice-pasture. With this trend, growers in the Gulf area have the necessary ingredients for successfully integrating soybeans with their rice operations and establishing the type of corporate complex that has paid off so well for the growers in Arkansas.

Both rice mills and grain processing plants, with all their machinery and equipment, represent an expensive undertaking for grower cooperatives. This must be considered in planning for an integration of the rice industry in the Gulf area of Louisiana and Texas.

Also, mills and plants must be strategically located and of sufficient size to realize economies of scale. An operation of this magnitude would require a large grower membership.

The current lack of a strong sales organization handling foreign sales for the Gulf area of Louisiana and Texas points up the need for a unified operation which can effectively export large volumes of rice from this area. Such an operation, accompanied by integration of drying, storing and milling, would materially strengthen rice markets in the Gulf area and improve grower returns.

A next step would be development of an effective sales structure in the U. S. rice industry through horizontal integration of all regional export sales agencies. A national rice marketing cooperative for export sales could eliminate any serious price fluctuations for U. S. rice sold in the overseas markets. Such a cooperative program for export sales of rice can operate under the authority granted by the Webb-Pomerene Act.

Considerations in Developing an Integrated Cooperative Marketing Program

A good processing and marketing operation combined into a single management system and operated on a farmer-owned and controlled basis is within reach of producers who are willing to coordinate their activities in a large-scale cooperative marketing program.

Interested growers can appoint a study committee to appraise the chances for a successful operation. The committee should study present operations in the industry, changes that have taken place and the potential of an integrated marketing program to meet the changes and correct current weaknesses. Emphasis should be given to volume, varieties and quality of rice; milling and storage facilities; marketing alternatives; financing and needed services.

After the economic need for the organization has been determined, answers to the following questions should assist the committee in evaluating the objectives, method of operation and member participation in the program:

I. Objectives of the program

What priority will be established for obtaining needed results such as higher returns to growers, reduced processing and marketing costs and wider sales distribution?

II. Facility requirements

A. What should be the approximate number and size of required processing and storage facilities and their strategic location for operational efficiency?

B. Will the organization own or lease transportation equipment?

III. Method of marketing

A. What plans can be agreed upon in achieving the transition between the current marketing method and the proposed method?

B. Will all sales outlets be served by the coordinated effort?

1. What is the minimum volume needed by the cooperative to satisfy its potential domestic and foreign sales outlets?

2. Should the cooperative's sales program be tied in with a regional export sales agency?

IV. Membership participation in program

A. How will the cooperative be organized and controlled?

B. What will be the procedure for admitting (or expelling) members?

C. What will be the provisions of the contract between the members and the organization?

D. What should be the quantity requirements, quality and grade specifications, duration of contract, payment plan, withdrawal period and penalties for noncompliance.

V. Method of financing

A. Can the cost of the program for facilities, sales and merchandising be approximated?

B. Will overhead and operational costs be met by initial capital, percent of sales, per unit charge or a combination of these methods?

C. What will be the effect of volume on cost?

D. Will change in volume cause a change in financing plans?

VI. Other factors for consideration

A. Will qualified leadership be available for the new program?

B. What will be the pricing policy?

C. Will returns to growers be made on a net pool or individual lot basis, or both?

D. Should a uniform cost accounting system be established for the organization?

E. Will the cooperative develop a new brand or obtain one on a franchise basis?

F. Should the cooperative purchase production and marketing supplies for its members?

G. Should marketing of rice and soybeans be integrated?

Findings of the survey committee should be presented to all prospective members. If they decide to establish an integrated marketing operation, an organizing committee should be selected to set up the program.

The organizing committee should retain the services of an attorney familiar with cooperative law to assist in drawing up the organization's legal papers. These include the articles of incorporation, bylaws and marketing agreement. The documents should be broad enough to assure operational flexibility.

In developing the plan of operation, special attention would need to be given to the following factors: Economies of scale in processing, market development, quality control, brand development, transportation, purchasing members' supplies, accounting and member relations.

The suggested cooperative integration of processing and marketing functions for the rice industry in the Gulf area can improve returns to grower members and better serve the demands of large buyers.

Other benefits might include: Improved quality of product; more adequate financing by aggregating resources; lower unit processing, sales and promotional costs; more orderly marketing of total production; better market distribution; higher sales value of production; and reduction in transportation and distribution costs.

BARGAINING ASSOCIATIONS

Bargaining associations are designed to bargain collectively with processors, suppliers and dealers without necessarily having to handle the product physically. Items subject to negotiation usually include prices, method and time of payment, delivery time and conditions, grades, sizes and other related matters.

Unlike labor unions, which have the protection of the Wagner Act in collective bargaining, farmers' bargaining associations have relatively no legal compulsory power over suppliers or produce buyers in bargaining collectively. A farmers' bargaining association must depend primarily on economic, rather than legal, persuasion at this time.

One approach would be to organize rice grower bargaining associations in subregions of the rice production areas of the U.S. with subsequent federation of subregional groups into a bargaining federation. This type of organization would permit more localized, personal relationships between rice growers and their organizations yet preserve the greater bargaining power of larger groupings.

Bargaining locals could be formed around existing co-op rice driers and/or rough rice marketing associations. In areas having no existing co-op associations, new locals expressly for bargaining purposes could be organized. In turn, these locals could be federated into a federation through existing cooperative associations or new ones.

The functions of a rice bargaining federation may be oriented into three levels or stages:

Stage I. The primary purpose at first would be to act as a clearinghouse of economic, statistical, price and market information and to coordinate the physical marketing and sale of rice in both domestic and export markets, or in export markets only.

Stage II. The second stage would embrace bargaining with rice buyers, millers, shippers and rice users of all types. Because of the price support mechanism for rice, the government loan price would serve as the base or floor price from which price bargaining would proceed. Acreage allotments and, subsequently, marketing quotas serve both as a barrier to entry and as a damper on excessive supplies.

Therefore, the main objective of a rice bargaining federation under those circumstances would be to negotiate for rice prices above the loan or support price. This situation is comparable to the negotiation by fluid milk co-ops for prices above the minimum federal order prices except that milk supplies are not controlled to the extent that rice supplies are controlled.

Stage III. A rice bargaining organization should move from the area of pure bargaining to physical operations of rice drying, milling, shipping and exporting of rice to some degree beyond what is currently being physically controlled by rice cooperatives. The rice cooperatives in Arkansas and California have already moved quite far into the physical handling and control of rice, and bargaining is hardly needed in these States. Louisiana, Mississippi and Texas rice co-ops have not moved as far in this regard.

218

Evaluating Rice Bargaining Potential

The possibilities of success of rice bargaining may be evaluated by the factors in Table 9-3.

In terms of the rice producer's welfare in strengthening his market position, bargaining evaluated on 25 different factors yields the following estimated results:

Rating	Number	Percent of total
Excellent prospects	3	12
Good prospects	9	36
Fair prospects	7	28
Poor prospects	6	24
Total	25	100

About 48 percent of the factors are rated good to excellent and 52 percent fair to poor. While these ratings are indeed rough estimates, the overall evaluation indicates some potential for rice bargaining. A federal law requiring prospective rice buyers to bargain collectively with rice producers or a rice marketing order made binding on handlers, coupled with present allotment-quota programs and a more vigorous co-op organization program in Louisiana, Mississippi and Texas, would improve the climate for rice bargaining. However, such legislation is not now available.

Producer Bargaining and Federal Marketing Orders

Rice is not an eligible commodity under the current Agricultural Marketing Agreement Act. It might be, however, included in future legislation providing there is strong industry support for such inclusion.

As shown in the Table 9-4, rice exhibits three characteristics highly associated with successful marketing orders: (1) End uses of markets with different price elasticities (domestic versus foreign markets), (2) concentrated and compact production area and (3) homogeneous products.

Rice exhibits three characteristics moderately (medium) associated with successful marketing orders: (1) No unregulated substitutes, (2) short-run adjustments in production difficult and (3) background of successful cooperative marketing.

Rice exhibits one important characteristic poorly associated with successful marketing orders: It is a storable commodity rather than a perishable regulated product.

The overall composite rating of rice as a likely product for successful marketing order regulation is high or excellent. The potential of rice producer bargaining associations would be enhanced

TABLE 9-3. FACTORS AFFECTING THE SUCCESS OF RICE BARGAINING IN TERMS OF RICE PRODUCERS' WELFARE

Factor	Evaluation of prospects in terms of grower welfare
1. Volume control	Good, if coupled with present allotment program.
2. Bargaining recognition	Poor, rice buyers are not legally obliged to recognize bargaining associations. New legislation needed here.
3. Skilled negotiators	Excellent, personnel available.
4. Restricted market entry	Good, allotment program is a barrier to entry.
5. Product substitutes	Poor, rice has many food substitutes.
6. Producer loyalty and understanding	Fair, Louisiana, Mississippi and Texas rice areas weak link in this regard; better in Arkansas and California.
7. Alternative uses	Good, producers have government loan program; operating co-ops and export markets.
8. Supply position	Good, rice supplies not burdensome. World food needs expanding.
9. Funds	Fair, rice growers can muster funds if bargaining purposes explained.
10. Nonmembers and lack of co-op organization	Fair, a serious problem in Louisiana and Texas, less in other areas.
11. Company-owned production	Good, rice buyers not prone to enter rice production themselves.
12. Inefficient producers	Good, small, inefficient growers are rapidly disappearing.
13. Legal protection	Poor, few legal ways to compel buyers to bargain with rice producer organizations.
14. Specialized outlets	Poor, rice must be milled or exported rough.
15. Producing to specifications	Poor, rice farmers tend to produce what they want to produce, not necessarily on specifications.
16. Area of production	Excellent, small, concentrated areas of rice output.
17. Expanding market demand	Fair, rice per capita consumption expands slowly if at all. Export market more favorable.
18. Product perishability	Excellent, rice storable.
19. Grower alternatives	Fair, rice farmers have only soybeans as main crop alternative. Some livestock alternatives.
20. Association leadership	Good, rice grower leadership above average.
21. Grower attitudes	Fair, many rice farmers believe government is sole alternative to industry problems.
22. Industry attitude	Poor, rice buyers probably much opposed to grower bargaining.
23. Public attitude	Fair, public not too concerned over rice bargaining.
24. Pricing structure	Good, rice grading, selling and marketing very variable, therefore, pricing efficiencies can be realized.
25. Threat of imports	Good, imports not a threat to domestic rice industry.

Source: Adapted from Roy, E. P., *Collective Bargaining in Agriculture*, Interstate Printers & Publishers, Inc., Danville, Ill. To be published.

TABLE 9-4. DEGREE TO WHICH SPECIFIED COMMODITIES EXHIBIT CHARACTERISTICS ASSOCIATED WITH SUCCESSFUL MARKETING ORDERS

Characteristic	Rice	Milk	Broilers	Hogs	Eggs	Turkeys	Lamb	Beef	Cotton	Corn	Wheat	Soybeans	Oats	Peanuts	Tobacco	Christmas trees	Sugar beets
End uses of markets with different price elasticity	1	1	3	3	2	3	3	3	2	2	1	2	3	1	2	3	3
Concentrated and compact production area	1	1	2	3	3	2	3	3	2	3	3	3	3	1	2	2	2
Homogeneous products	1	1	1	3	1	1	2	3	2	1	2	1	1	2	2	2	1
No unregulated substitutes	2	2	3	3	1	3	3	3	3	3	2	3	3	2	1	1	3
Shortrun adjustments in production are difficult	2	2	3	3	3	3	2	2	2	3	2	3	3	2	2	2	2
Background of successful cooperative marketing	2	1	3	3	2	2	2	3	2	3	2	3	3	2	1	2	2
Perishable regulated product	3	1	1	1	2	1	1	1	3	3	3	3	3	3	3	1	1
Degree to which commodity exhibits characteristics related to successful orders (composite)	1	1	2	3	2	2	2	3	2	3	2	3	3	1	1	2	2

1 = High   2 = Medium   3 = Low

Source: Babb, E. M. and others, *Federal Market Orders: Present and Potential Uses*, Indiana Agricultural Extension Service. Mimeo EC-238, Layafette, Ind., December 1961, p. 10.

under the cover of marketing orders and/or acreage allotment-marketing quota legislation.

Organizations for Dissemination of Marketing Information

In recent years, there has been a tendency for farmers and farm groups to organize for disseminating of marketing, price and economic information for "clearinghouse" purposes. The main objective of such organizations has been to alleviate the accumulation of surpluses in one area and deficits in another, thereby stabilizing prices. Secondary objectives have included voluntary production cutbacks, more efficient price discovery and better bargaining over prices.

One rather successful example of such co-op clearinghouse associations is the National Egg Company (NEC), Atlanta, Georgia, a cooperative organized under the farmer cooperative laws of Georgia.

It has two major objectives: (1) To serve as a clearinghouse on who is long or short on particular grades of eggs in the area, and (2) in the event there is a surplus or shortage of eggs of a particular

221

grade, to move eggs to markets other than New York City or to help obtain the grade or grades of eggs whch are short from other areas, including New York City.

Its members are marketers but also produce many of the eggs they market. Almost half the eggs produced in the Southeast are represented by NEC.[25]

Officials of NEC report that the organization of this cooperative has resulted in a return of about 1 cent per dozen more for table eggs produced and sold for members. This amounts to about a 3 percent price increase.[26]

A clearinghouse producer association or associations in the rice industry would offer potentials in collecting and disseminating rough rice prices on a regular basis by centralizing such activities in one central office, possibly wtih computerized facilities and hook-ups with various field price-reporting and other data-gathering points.

In addition to centralized price gathering and disseminating activities, other rice clearinghouse activities might include information on long and short-positions in rice stocks and inventories and the proper allocation of rice supplies to market demands both domestic and for export.

---

[25]Davis, D., "What Is the National Egg Company?" *Poultry Tribune,* Cullman, Alabama, May 1967, pp. 20-21, 78.

[26]Sledge, C. B., "The National Egg Company," *Louisiana Poultry Professional Workers Society Meeting,* Baton Rouge, Louisiana, February 28, 1967.